THE TIMES TOP 100 GRADUATE EMPLOYERS

The definitive guide to the leading employers
recruiting graduates during 2019-2020.

HIGH FLIERS

HIGH FLIERS PUBLICATIONS LTD
IN ASSOCIATION WITH THE TIMES

Published by High Fliers Publications Limited
The Gridiron Building, 1 Pancras Square, London, N1C 4AG
Telephone: 020 7428 9100   *Web:* www.Top100GraduateEmployers.com

Editor Martin Birchall
Publisher Gill Thomas
Production Manager Jeremy Brown
Portrait Photography Tatjana Panek

Printed and bound in Italy by L.E.G.O. S.p.A.

A CIP catalogue record for this book
is available from the British Library.
ISBN 978-1-9160401-0-6

Contents

Foreword

By **Martin Birchall**
Editor, *The Times Top 100 Graduate Employers*

Welcome to the 2019-2020 edition of *The Times Top 100 Graduate Employers*, your annual guide to the UK's most prestigious and sought-after graduate employers.

Standing on the steps of 10 Downing Street, just a few days after Boris Johnson became Prime Minister, there was a palpable sense of the political turmoil that has gripped the country.

The EU referendum, two General Elections, three Prime Ministers in three years, and the protracted Brexit process have thrust politics – and the way the nation is governed – into the spotlight in a way that hasn't happened for a generation.

This hasn't just dominated the agenda at Westminster and the nation's conversation, it has also made a lasting impact on university students and the graduate job market too.

The number of new graduates applying to work in the public sector is now at its highest level for almost a decade. And, for a record proportion of those leaving university in the summer of 2019, 'giving something back to society' was a key priority for their first graduate job.

This imperative to shape the future of the country for the better means that, for the first time in a decade and a half, new graduates have named the Civil Service as the UK's number one graduate employer in this edition of *The Times*

> **"** *The opportunity to shape policy and work at the heart of Government proved irresistible to the 'Class of 2019'.* **"**

Top 100 Graduate Employers. The opportunity to shape policy and work at the heart of Government proved irresistible to the 'Class of 2019', who made an uprecedented number of applications for places on its acclaimed Fast Stream programme.

And in a remarkable achievement, all five of the inspirational programmes that are transforming society by recruiting outstanding graduates to work in teaching, social work, policing and the prison service – Teach First, Frontline, Think Ahead, Police Now and Unlocked – are now ranked in the UK's top fifty graduate employers.

Together, the public sector employers featured in *The Times Top 100 Graduate Employers* are recruiting over 5,000 graduates in 2020, twice the number of vacancies available a decade ago.

For the third year running, the Civil Service Fast Stream will be offering more than 1,200 places, and the NHS is set to double recruitment for its well-respected management training scheme this year.

Teach First recruited 1,735 trainee teachers in 2019, the biggest-ever annual intake for a graduate employer in the UK, and is preparing to take on even more new recruits in 2020.

But it's not just the public sector that is offering exciting opportunities for new graduates. Despite all of the uncertainty that Brexit has brought over the last three years, the number of graduate jobs at the country's top employers has actually grown by almost 15 per cent since 2017, with more entry-level roles available in technology, at the leading accounting & professional services firms, and even in the rapidly-changing retail sector.

And the outlook for 2020 is resolutely upbeat too for many of the UK's top graduate employers. From the City's investment banks and elite international law firms, to the country's best-known engineering & industrial companies, their continuing commitment to graduate recruitment is about investing in the people their organisations will need for the next ten or twenty years, not just filling vacancies for next September.

Since the first edition was published in 1999, more than a million copies of *The Times Top 100 Graduate Employers* have been produced, to help students and graduates at universities across the UK research their career options and find their first graduate job. Two decades on, the *Top 100* continues to provide an unrivalled, independent assessment of the country's most highly-regarded graduate employers.

This year's rankings have been compiled from the results of face-to-face interviews with almost 20,000 final year students who graduated from undergraduate degree courses at UK universities in the summer of 2019.

Students were asked to identify the employer that they thought offered the best opportunities for new graduates and, between them, the 'Class of 2019' named organisations in every major industry, business sector and employment area. The one hundred employers that were mentioned most often during the research are ranked to form *The Times Top 100 Graduate Employers* for 2019-2020.

This book is therefore a celebration of the employers who are judged to offer the brightest prospects for new graduates. Whether through the perceived quality of their training programmes, their commercial success, the scale of their graduate recruitment, or by the impression that their on-campus promotions made, these are the employers that were most attractive to graduate job hunters in 2019.

The Times Top 100 Graduate Employers won't necessarily identify which organisation you should join after graduation – only you can decide that. But it is an invaluable reference if you want to discover what the UK's leading employers are offering for new graduates in 2020.

THE TIMES TOP 100 GRADUATE EMPLOYERS
Finding out about the Top 100 Graduate Employers

IN PRINT

Each employer featured in this edition of the *Top 100* has their own **Employer Entry**, providing details of graduate vacancies for 2020, minimum academic requirements, starting salaries, and the universities employers will be visiting in 2019-2020.

ONLINE

Register now with the official Top 100 website for full access to the very latest information about the UK's most sought-after graduate employers.

And get ready for your applications, interviews and assessment centres with up-to-the-minute business news about each of the organisations featured in this year's *Top 100*.

www.Top100GraduateEmployers.com

BY EMAIL

Once you've registered with the Top 100 website, you'll receive **weekly email bulletins** with news of the employers you're interested in, their careers events at your university, and their forthcoming application deadlines.

**Civil Service
Fast Stream**

Be Yourself
Make a Difference

Be a Fast Streamer

No other UK employer can offer you the opportunity to make a difference to the whole of society. Giving back has never felt so rewarding.

faststream.gov.uk

THE TIMES
TOP 100
GRADUATE EMPLOYERS

**GRADUATE EMPLOYER
OF THE YEAR 2019**

Civil Service Fast Stream

Be Yourself
Be a Future Leader
Be a Fast Streamer

Our leadership programme is as unique as you are. Your Fast Stream journey will be one of a kind.

faststream.gov.uk

security policy coordinator assistant private secretary to a chief scientific advisor governance and reporting manager internal communications officer implementation lead research officer risks and issues manager IT operations manager job centre customer service manager data scientist project delivery specialists contract manager associate delivery manager project sponsor science and technology development lead (security and defence) commercial manager programme manager / director clerk of printing business analyst project manager / director stakeholder engagement manager assistant economist procurement manager senior campaigns manager SDIP intern policy advisor (science and innovation) head of profession statistician engagement manager communications manager category manager business case manager financial accountant EDIP intern advisor assistant finance business partner/finance

configuration analyst EU exit financial reporting of petitions financial planning manager strategic

Civil Service
Fast Stream

business partner manager data policy advisor executive clerk press officer officer benefits communication and

marketing officer finance analyst portfolio analyst implementation manager finance manager project manager internal auditor project support officer junior cyber analyst resource accounts analyst economic adviser senior assurance officer corporate governance adviser financial strategy advisor portfolio manager / director engagement and events executive business change manager commercial capability manager business analyst commercial capability manager senior responsible officer junior service designer business analysis & change stakeholder manager data scientist PMO manager / director procurement manager select committee media officer EDIP intern project planner financial accountant assurance manager strategic relationships manager senior project manager

THE TIMES TOP 100 GRADUATE EMPLOYERS 2011-2012

THE TIMES TOP 100 GRADUATE EMPLOYERS 2012-2013

THE TIMES TOP 100 GRADUATE EMPLOYERS 2013-2014

THE TIMES TOP 100 GRADUATE EMPLOYERS 2014-2015

THE TIMES TOP 100 GRADUATE EMPLOYERS 2015-2016

THE TIMES TOP 100 GRADUATE EMPLOYERS 2016-2017

THE TIMES TOP 100 GRADUATE EMPLOYERS 2017-2018

THE TIMES TOP 100 GRADUATE EMPLOYERS 2018-2019

THE TIMES TOP 100 GRADUATE EMPLOYERS 2019-2020

Researching The Times Top 100 Graduate Employers

By **Gill Thomas**
Publisher, High Fliers Publications

There were an estimated five thousand employers, large and small, recruiting graduates from the UK's leading universities when the first edition of *The Times Top 100 Graduate Employers* was published in 1999.

For students researching their career options, finding the 'right' graduate employer was often a daunting prospect. What basis could you use to evaluate such a large number of different organisations and the opportunities they offered for new graduates after university?

Twenty years on, the number of employers recruiting graduates has increased considerably and there are now an estimated 200,000 jobs available annually.

How, then, can anyone produce a meaningful league table of the UK's top graduate employers? Which criteria define whether one individual organisation is 'better' than another?

For the last two decades, *The Times Top 100 Graduate Employers* has been compiled annually by the independent market research company, High Fliers Research, through face-to-face on-campus interviews with final year students at the country's leading universities.

This latest edition is based on research with 19,712 new graduates who left universities across the UK in the summer of 2019. The research examined students' experiences during their search for a first graduate job, and asked them about their attitudes to employers.

Finalists from the 'Class of 2019' who took part in the study were selected at random to represent the full cross-section of final year students at their universities, not just those who had already secured graduate employment.

"This year marks the first change at the top of The Times Top 100 Graduate Employers for a decade and a half."

The question used to produce the *Top 100* rankings was "Which employer do you think offers the best opportunities for graduates?" The question was deliberately open-ended and students were not shown a list of employers to choose from or prompted in any way during the interview.

Within the full survey sample, final year students named more than 1,600 different organisations – from new start-up businesses and small local or regional employers, to some of the world's best-known companies. The responses were analysed and the one hundred organisations that were mentioned most often make up *The Times Top 100 Graduate Employers* for 2019.

The considerable selection of answers given by finalists from the 'Class of 2019' shows that students used several different criteria to determine which employer offered the best opportunities for graduates. Many evaluated employers based on the information they had seen

THE TIMES TOP 100 GRADUATE EMPLOYERS
The Times Top 100 Graduate Employers 2019

	2018			2018	
1	2	CIVIL SERVICE	51	70	BT
2	1	PWC	52	61	EXXONMOBIL
3	3	ALDI	53	78	ROYAL NAVY
4	5	GOOGLE	54	91	SIEMENS
5	7	NHS	55	79	MI5 - THE SECURITY SERVICE
6	8	KPMG	56	35	M&S
7	6	DELOITTE	57	41	MARS
8	4	TEACH FIRST	58	60	SLAUGHTER AND MAY
9	12	BBC	59	85	L'ORÉAL
10	13	J.P. MORGAN	60	NEW	UBS
11	9	EY	61	100	AECOM
12	14	HSBC	62	59	BLOOMBERG
13	11	UNILEVER	63	65	BAKER MCKENZIE
14	10	GSK	64	73	LOCAL GOVERNMENT
15	16	ROLLS-ROYCE	65	56	SANTANDER
16	17	GOLDMAN SACHS	66	48	HERBERT SMITH FREEHILLS
17	18	BARCLAYS	67	54	BOOTS
18	23	AMAZON	68	67	WELLCOME
19	34	NEWTON	69	69	CITI
20	21	MCKINSEY & COMPANY	70	71	BANK OF ENGLAND
21	25	IBM	71	83	RAF
22	22	BP	72	81	NETWORK RAIL
23	24	LLOYDS BANKING GROUP	73	33	JOHN LEWIS PARTNERSHIP
24	15	LIDL	74	52	ASOS
25	31	RBS	75	57	VIRGIN MEDIA
26	36	CLIFFORD CHANCE	76	58	DLA PIPER
27	20	ACCENTURE	77	72	BLACKROCK
28	49	MICROSOFT	78	66	BAIN & COMPANY
29	29	SHELL	79	75	TPP
30	28	ARMY	80	88	DEUTSCHE BANK
31	32	PROCTER & GAMBLE	81	NEW	BDO
32	38	ALLEN & OVERY	82	55	FACEBOOK
33	19	JAGUAR LAND ROVER	83	62	FRESHFIELDS BRUCKHAUS DERINGER
34	27	ARUP	84	99	PINSENT MASONS
35	47	BOSTON CONSULTING GROUP	85	94	NESTLÉ
36	42	THINK AHEAD	86	NEW	HUAWEI
37	39	BAE SYSTEMS	87	NEW	VODAFONE
38	30	SKY	88	68	MCDONALD'S
39	44	APPLE	89	76	HOGAN LOVELLS
40	51	AIRBUS	90	89	CMS
41	43	MORGAN STANLEY	91	96	CHARITYWORKS
42	26	FRONTLINE	92	NEW	NORTON ROSE FULBRIGHT
43	45	ATKINS	93	80	WHITE & CASE
44	53	PENGUIN RANDOM HOUSE	94	95	IRWIN MITCHELL
45	40	LINKLATERS	95	NEW	GCHQ
46	46	ASTRAZENECA	96	NEW	ADMIRAL
47	90	POLICE NOW	97	NEW	MOTT MACDONALD
48	37	TESCO	98	77	JOHNSON & JOHNSON
49	NEW	UNLOCKED	99	86	GRANT THORNTON
50	50	DYSON	100	NEW	ENTERPRISE RENT-A-CAR

Source **High Fliers Research** 19,712 final year students leaving UK universities in the summer of 2019 were asked the open-ended question "Which employer do you think offers the best opportunities for graduates?" during interviews for *The UK Graduate Careers Survey 2019*

during their job search – the quality of on-campus recruitment promotions, the impression formed from meeting employers' representatives, or their experiences during the application and selection process.

Some focused on employers' general reputations and their public image, their business profile or commercial success. Finalists also considered the level of graduate vacancies available within individual organisations.

Other final year students, however, used the 'employment proposition' as their main guide – the quality of graduate training and development an employer offers, the starting salary and remuneration package available, and the practical aspects of a first graduate job, such as location or working hours.

Irrespective of the criteria that students used to arrive at their answer, the hardest part for many was just selecting a single organisation. To some extent, choosing two or three, or even half a dozen employers, would have been much easier. But the whole purpose of the exercise was to replicate the reality that everyone faces – you can only work for one organisation and, at each stage of the graduate job search, there are choices to be made as to which direction to take and which employers to pursue.

The resulting *Top 100* is a dynamic league table of the UK's most exciting and well-respected graduate employers.

This year marks the first change at the top of *The Times Top 100 Graduate Employers* for a decade and a half. In the closest result for eleven years, the Civil Service has been named the UK's leading graduate employer by a margin of just eight votes, moving up one place from last year's number two position. Best known for its prestigious Fast Stream programme, the Civil Service's share of the vote has doubled over the past three years and has risen by more than a quarter in just the last twelve months. The Civil Service Fast Stream is currently recruiting more than a thousand graduates annually, its highest-ever intake.

PwC, the accounting and professional services firm that was number one for the last fifteen years, is in a close second place. Aldi's popular trainee area manager programme remains in third place, just ahead of internet giant Google, which moves up to fourth place after three years at number five. The NHS graduate management programme returns to the top five for the first time since 2014.

'Big Four' accounting & professional services firms KPMG and Deloitte are separated by just two votes in sixth and seventh places, but rival firm EY has slipped out of the top ten for only the second time in a decade.

The Teach First programme has dropped back four places to 8th place, but investment bank J.P. Morgan climbs three places to its best-ever ranking of 10th place, and Amazon moves up another five places to appear in the top twenty for the first time. After joining the *Top 100* in 2013, consulting firm Newton has risen more than fifty places in just three years and has jumped to 19th place this year.

Seven of the ten retailers listed in this year's *Top 100* have dropped back in the rankings, and there have been mixed fortunes for the fourteen law firms that feature within the new *Top 100*. Clifford Chance has climbed ten places to 26th place, its best ranking for a decade, and five more firms – Allen & Overy, Slaughter and May, Baker McKenzie, Pinsent Masons and Irwin Mitchell – have each improved their positions this year. But seven firms have dropped back in the rankings, including Freshfields Bruckhaus Deringer, DLA Piper and Herbert Smith Freehills.

The highest climbers in the new *Top 100* are led by Police Now – the programme that recruits graduates to work in police forces across the UK – which has jumped an impressive forty-three places to 47th place. Professional & technical services companies AECOM and Siemens have both climbed more than thirty places. L'Oréal has bounced back up twenty-six places, after a drop of sixty-one places in *The Times Top 100 Graduate Employers* in 2018. And the Royal Navy has climbed twenty-five places to reach its best ranking for five years.

Two of the year's biggest falls are Jaguar Land Rover, which has dropped out of the top twenty to 33rd place, and the John Lewis Partnership, which has fallen forty places after cancelling its graduate recruitment in 2018.

There are a total of ten new entries or re-entries in this year's *Top 100*, the highest being Unlocked – the recently-launched programme that recruits graduates to work in the prison service. It is ranked in 49th place, the highest *Top 100* debut for a new recruiter for sixteen years. Investment bank UBS is a re-entry in 60th place, and accounting & professional services firm BDO is back in 81st place, having slipped out of the *Top 100* in 2018.

Wales' largest private sector employer – insurance company Admiral – is a new entry in 96th place, and global technology group Huawei and

Get ahead of the curve.

Graduate and undergraduate opportunities

It's always good to get a head start. And thanks to Launch Pad, you could be starting your career journey in Audit, Tax & Pensions, Consulting, Deal Advisory, Technology & Engineering or KPMG Business Services sooner than you think.

Launch Pad is an innovative approach to graduate recruitment. A one-day event at the final stage of the process, it could see you being offered a role within as little as two working days. An interactive experience, it will give you the opportunity to demonstrate your talents through assessment activities and interviews with senior members of our team. Plus, you'll gain new skills, meet lots of people and find out more about the many opportunities at KPMG in the UK. Apply now.

kpmgcareers.co.uk

Anticipate tomorrow. Deliver today.

Enterprise Rent-a-Car are listed in the *Top 100* for the first time in 86th and 100th places respectively.

After an absence of nine years, Vodafone has rejoined the *Top 100* in 87th place, and law firm Norton Rose Fulbright, intelligence and security organisation GCHQ, and engineering company Mott MacDonald have each returned to the *Top 100* after dropping out of last year's rankings.

Employers leaving the *Top 100* in 2019 include BMW, Cancer Research UK, advertising group WPP, pharmaceuticals company Pfizer, British Airways, professional services firm Aon, property company Savills, Lloyd's insurance market, and consumer goods companies Mondelēz International and Danone.

In the two decades since the original edition of *The Times Top 100 Graduate Employers* was published, just three organisations have made it to number one in the rankings. Andersen Consulting (now Accenture) held onto the top spot for the first four years, and its success heralded a huge surge in popularity for careers in consulting. At its peak in 2001, almost one in six graduates applied for jobs in the sector.

In the year before the firm changed its name from Andersen Consulting to Accenture, it astutely introduced a new graduate package that included a £28,500 starting salary (a sky-high

figure for graduates in 2000) and a much talked-about £10,000 bonus, helping to assure the firm's popularity, irrespective of its corporate branding.

In 2003, after two dismal years in graduate recruitment when vacancies for university-leavers dropped by more than a fifth following the terrorist attacks of 11th September 2001, the Civil Service was named Britain's leading graduate employer.

Just twelve months later it was displaced by PricewaterhouseCoopers, the accounting and professional services firm formed from the merger of Price Waterhouse and Coopers & Lybrand in 1998. At the time, the firm was the largest private-sector recruiter of graduates, with an intake in 2004 of more than a thousand trainees.

Now known simply as PwC, the firm remained at number one for an impressive fifteen years, increasing its share of the student vote from 5 per cent in 2004 to more than 10 per cent in 2007, and fighting off the stiffest of competition from rivals Deloitte in 2008, when just seven votes separated the two employers.

PwC's reign as the UK's leading graduate employer represented a real renaissance for the entire accounting & professional services sector. Twenty years ago, a career in accountancy was regarded as a safe, traditional employment choice, whereas today's profession is viewed in a very

TOP 100 — Number Ones, Movers & Shakers in the Top 100

	NUMBER ONES		HIGHEST CLIMBING EMPLOYERS		HIGHEST NEW ENTRIES
1999	ANDERSEN CONSULTING	1999	SCHLUMBERGER (UP 13 PLACES)	1999	PFIZER (31st)
2000	ANDERSEN CONSULTING	2000	CAPITAL ONE (UP 32 PLACES)	2000	MORGAN STANLEY (34th)
2001	ACCENTURE	2001	EUROPEAN COMMISSION (UP 36 PLACES)	2001	MARCONI (36th)
2002	ACCENTURE	2002	WPP (UP 36 PLACES)	2002	GUINNESS UDV (44th)
2003	CIVIL SERVICE	2003	ROLLS-ROYCE (UP 37 PLACES)	2003	ASDA (40th)
2004	PRICEWATERHOUSECOOPERS	2004	J.P. MORGAN (UP 29 PLACES)	2004	BAKER & MCKENZIE (61st)
2005	PRICEWATERHOUSECOOPERS	2005	TEACH FIRST (UP 22 PLACES)	2005	PENGUIN (70th)
2006	PRICEWATERHOUSECOOPERS	2006	GOOGLE (UP 32 PLACES)	2006	FUJITSU (81st)
2007	PRICEWATERHOUSECOOPERS	2007	PFIZER (UP 30 PLACES)	2007	BDO STOY HAYWARD (74th)
2008	PRICEWATERHOUSECOOPERS	2008	CO-OPERATIVE GROUP (UP 39 PLACES)	2008	SKY (76th)
2009	PRICEWATERHOUSECOOPERS	2009	CADBURY (UP 48 PLACES)	2009	BDO STOY HAYWARD (68th)
2010	PRICEWATERHOUSECOOPERS	2010	ASDA (UP 41 PLACES)	2010	SAATCHI & SAATCHI (49th)
2011	PWC	2011	CENTRICA (UP 41 PLACES)	2011	APPLE (53rd)
2012	PWC	2012	NESTLÉ (UP 44 PLACES)	2012	EUROPEAN COMMISSION (56th)
2013	PWC	2013	DFID (UP 40 PLACES)	2013	SIEMENS (70th)
2014	PWC	2014	TRANSPORT FOR LONDON (UP 36 PLACES)	2014	FRONTLINE (76th)
2015	PWC	2015	DIAGEO, NEWTON (UP 43 PLACES)	2015	DANONE (66th)
2016	PWC	2016	BANK OF ENGLAND (UP 34 PLACES)	2016	SANTANDER (63rd)
2017	PWC	2017	CANCER RESEARCH UK (UP 38 PLACES)	2017	DYSON (52nd)
2018	PWC	2018	MCDONALD'S (UP 30 PLACES)	2018	ASOS (52nd)
2019	CIVIL SERVICE	2019	POLICE NOW (UP 43 PLACES)	2019	UNLOCKED (49th)

Source High Fliers Research

NEVER NOT PUTTING CLIENTS ON THE RIGHT TRACK.
NEVER NOT NEWTON.

It's good to leave a lasting legacy. And that's something Newton graduates do from the day they join. On one recent project with a train manufacturer, for instance, they helped to slash the build time of each train from 2,000 hours to fewer than 900. And, in doing so, they rescued one of the UK's oldest manufacturing sites.

Find out more at **WorkAtNewton.com**

different light. The training required to become a chartered accountant is now seen as a prized business qualification, and the sector's leading firms are regularly described as 'dynamic' and 'international' by undergraduates looking for their first job after university.

A total of 213 different organisations have now appeared within *The Times Top 100 Graduate Employers* since its inception, and forty of these have made it into the rankings every year since 1999. The most consistent performers have been PwC, KPMG and the Civil Service, each of which have never been lower than 9th place in the league table. The NHS has also had a formidable record, appearing in every top ten since 2003, while the BBC, Goldman Sachs and EY (formerly Ernst & Young) have all remained within the top twenty throughout the last decade.

Google is the highest-climbing employer within the *Top 100*, having risen over eighty places during the last decade, to reach the top three for the first time in 2015. But car manufacturer Jaguar Land Rover holds the record for the fastest-moving employer, after jumping more than seventy places in just five years, between 2009 and 2014.

Other employers haven't been so successful. British Airways ranked in 6th place in 1999 but dropped out of the *Top 100* altogether a decade later, and Ford, which was once rated as high as 14th, disappeared out of the list in 2006 after cancelling its graduate recruitment programme two years previously. A more recent high-ranking casualty is Sainsbury's, which – having reached 18th in 2003 – tumbled out of the *Top 100* in 2016.

Thirty graduate employers – including Nokia, Maersk, the Home Office, Cable & Wireless,

THE TIMES TOP 100 GRADUATE EMPLOYERS
Winners & Losers in the Top 100

MOST CONSISTENT EMPLOYERS	HIGHEST RANKING	LOWEST RANKING
ANDERSEN (FORMERLY ARTHUR ANDERSEN)	2nd (1999-2001)	3rd (2002)
PWC	1st (2004-2018)	3rd (1999-2001, 2003)
KPMG	3rd (2006-2008, 2011-2012)	9th (2015)
CIVIL SERVICE	1st (2003, 2019)	8th (2011)
BBC	5th (2005-2007)	14th (1999)
GSK	10th (2017-2018)	22nd (2002-2003)
IBM	13th (2000)	25th (2017-2018)
EY (FORMERLY ERNST & YOUNG)	7th (2013)	20th (2001)
BP	14th (2013-2014)	32nd (2004)
GOLDMAN SACHS	5th (2001)	25th (1999)

EMPLOYERS CLIMBING HIGHEST	NEW ENTRY RANKING	HIGHEST RANKING
GOOGLE	85th (2005)	3rd (2015)
LIDL	89th (2009)	13th (2017)
NEWTON	94th (2013)	19th (2019)
JAGUAR LAND ROVER	87th (2009)	16th (2014)
ALDI	65th (2002)	2nd (2015-2016)
AMAZON	81st (2015)	18th (2019)
MI5 – THE SECURITY SERVICE	96th (2007)	33rd (2010)
TEACH FIRST	63rd (2003)	2nd (2014)
APPLE	87th (2009)	27th (2012)
ATKINS	94th (2004)	37th (2009)

EMPLOYERS FALLING FURTHEST	HIGHEST RANKING	LOWEST RANKING
BRITISH AIRWAYS	6th (1999)	Not ranked (2010, 2011, 2017, 2019)
FORD	11th (1999)	Not ranked (FROM 2006)
UBS	17th (2002)	Not ranked (2018)
SAINSBURY'S	18th (2003)	Not ranked (FROM 2016)
THOMSON REUTERS	22nd (2001)	Not ranked (2009-2012, FROM 2014)
ASTRAZENECA	24th (2003)	Not ranked (2012-2014)
ASDA	27th (2004)	Not ranked (FROM 2016)
BANK OF AMERICA MERRILL LYNCH	27th (2000)	Not ranked (FROM 2017)
RAF	32nd (2005)	Not ranked (2015)
MINISTRY OF DEFENCE	35th (2003)	Not ranked (2007, FROM 2012)

Source High Fliers Research

United Biscuits, Nationwide, Capgemini and the Met Office – have the dubious record of having only been ranked in the *Top 100* once during the last fifteen years. And Marconi had the unusual distinction of being one of the highest-ever new entries, in 36th place in 2001, only to vanish from the list entirely the following year.

One of the most spectacular ascendancies in the *Top 100* has been the rise of the discount retailer Aldi, which joined the list in 65th place in 2002, rose to 3rd place in 2009 – helped in part by its memorable remuneration package for new recruits (currently £44,000 plus an Audi A4 or BMW 3 Series car) – and was ranked in 2nd place in both 2015 and 2016. Teach First, which appeared as a new entry at 63rd place in 2003, climbed the rankings every year for a decade, and reached 2nd place in the *Top 100* in 2014.

This year's edition of *The Times Top 100 Graduate Employers* has produced a number of dramatic changes in the rankings, and the results provide a unique insight into how graduates from the 'Class of 2019' rated the UK's leading employers.

THE TIMES TOP 100 GRADUATE EMPLOYERS
The UK's Number 1 Graduate Employer 2019

"It means everything to us that the Civil Service has been named the UK's number one graduate employer in *The Times Top 100 Graduate Employers* for 2019.

The Civil Service Fast Stream has a very long and distinguished history of recruiting the leaders of the future for Whitehall's Government departments and the wider Civil Service.

But over the last three years we've worked tirelessly to improve our recruitment processes, to ensure that diversity and inclusion are at the heart of what we do, and to make sure that the Fast Stream stays accessible and relevant to today's graduates from all backgrounds.

Greg Hobbs, Head of the Civil Service Fast Stream 2016-2019

This is a crucial time for the Civil Service and the country. Graduates joining the Fast Stream have the chance to be part of this, bringing their own fresh thinking to delivering the agenda of the day for the nation, and experiencing the decision-making process first-hand.

To rise to these challenges, the Fast Stream programme has expanded significantly. When I became a Fast Streamer in 2005, there were fewer than 200 places available annually across the Civil Service, whereas last year's intake reached 1,500 for the first time, with places available in fifteen different areas, from the Diplomatic Service to finance, human resources and digital, data & technology.

It's still a competitive selection process and this year's programme attracted the broadest range of candidates yet, with around 56,000 applications. But we've shortened the recruitment timetable and had a record number of our current Fast Streamers out on campus to help students really understand what it takes to be successful in the Civil Service.

We're very proud that today's Civil Service Fast Stream is the most diverse it has ever been. But we continue to strive to make sure that the Fast Stream reflects every part of society that the Civil Service serves.

The Fast Stream is about delivering leadership for the future. We need great leaders, not just for now or the next three or four years, but for ten or fifteen years from now. We are recruiting graduates who are willing to build and be part of a lifelong learning culture that will take the Civil Service and the country through the changes that the next generation will face. It's an exciting future."

Chartered Accountants change the world

Over 9,000 ICAEW Chartered Accountants play a vital role in helping charities to raise and make the most of funds that can save lives. So if you want to make a difference while making a living, then you can use your skills to support the things you really care about.

More than you'd imagine
icaew.com/careers

The experience stays with you

We've got lots of different work experience programmes for every year of study, so you can learn more about our business and boost your employability.

They'll help you make an informed decision about which of our career opportunities is best for you. If you do well you could even be fast-tracked to a graduate role.

Join us. We're focused on helping you reach your full potential.

Take the opportunity of a lifetime
pwc.co.uk/ work-experience

f PwCCareersUK

in pwc-uk

○ pwc_uk_careers

You careerspwc

🐦 @pwc_uk_careers

pwc

Boost your employability....

Office Open Events
1 day

Students of all years.

Females of the Future
1 day

First and second year students.

NI Talent Academy
2 days

First and second year students.

Women in Business
3 days | Paid

Students of all years.

Summer Internships
6-8 weeks | Paid

Penultimate year students.

Work Placements
6-11 months | Paid

Undergraduate and graduate students.

Graduate jobs boosted despite Brexit concerns

CALLUM KEOWN
@CallumKeown1

The investment banking sector is set to offer the most generous starting salaries, with an average of £47,000,

THE UK's top employers are set to boost gradua...
per cent this...
uncertainty ov...

The country...
employers ha...
recruitment...
in 2019, acc...
ed by resear...

It comes...
vacancies in...
erendum an...

...and consulting firms

Graduate salaries stall but Brexit creates more jobs

Rosemary Bennett Education Editor

There will be more jobs for those graduating from university t...
mer than at any time in the pa...
despite the uncertainty ove...
according to an annual surv...
100 top employers in Britain.

Between them the companie...
hire a total of 22,181 graduates th...
a 9.1 per cent increase over last y...
the biggest year-on-year...
...duate recruitment since 2...

Deringer and Hogan Lovells, all offering £45,000. Also high in the salary rankings are the consultants Newton

---

Highest salary for graduates is £60k

THE top graduate starting salary has risen to £60,000, an annual survey shows.

The...ay packet – £10,000 up on...
...offered by investment...
...the £30,000 average for...
...first jobs.

...sector was charity, at...
...by the public sector, th...
...ng employers included...
...raduates £44,000 a year...
...ing City law firms.

...f High Fliers Research,...
...t the study, said: 'The...
...ket dipped two y...

Brexit boom for graduates as civil service boosts its ranks

Rosemary Bennett Education Editor

5,268 vacancies in the public sector for those leaving university, compared...
...th 4,850 in...
...next

which are offering £46,000; and Aldi, which offers graduate trainees £44,000
...di A4 com... ...car.

Graduates promised high-flying success

Telford-based Encore Person-recruitment by more than 10 per...
...2018.

...a vast number of stu-
...to enter the job market
...core wants to change
...cs, highlighting re-
...a rewarding and
...career opportunity.
...ich has an office in
...duced the e-grads
...ew recruits. With

a variety of job roles on offer, man...at Encore Per...
from...
sche...
in-ha...
day-t...
scher...
terna...
caree...
will f...
edge...
in rec...

Students told not to obsess over finding job

Stressed graduates should take six months off after university, says Ucas chief

By Harry Yorke

STUDENTS should not feel compelled to get a job until six months after graduating, the outgoing head of Ucas has said in a warning against the "obsession" with careers.

Universities and middle-class parents have become "too fixated" with using their degrees to get a job, suggested Mary Curnock Cook, of the Universities and Colleges Admissions Service.

Instead, parents should encourage their children to move back home and explore their options before embarking on a career.

Speaking to *The Daily Telegraph* in one of her final interviews before step-

go to university and then land a career straight after that. It's terribly unhelpful.

"Students may need...ke some down-time after the stre...and dissertations. I don...
any harm in doing tempo...
or non-graduate work...
before finding something...
nent."

Her comments come...
growing competition in...
ket, as employers stru...
between graduate appli...
record proportion – thre...
ceiving a degree classifi...
better last year.

The Higher Education

Jobs boost hope for graduates

dents repeatedly talked about their anxiety of finding employment after studying.

The number of unemployed grads hits 30-year low

Brexit-related uncertainty has tempted graduates into postgrad courses, but the jo...

David Benady

...ome 300,000 students...
...ross...

graduate labour market has held up well despite the economic an...

as an English-language assistant in a village in...
...Sin...
...JE...
...for...

Graduates will compete for fewer jobs as firms cut back

take on school-leavers. Martin Birchall, managing director of High Fliers, ...hich compiles the data for the report, ...d that many employers had at-...ted a "business as usual" approach ...ate recruitment since the Brex-...ut were now more cautious. ...petition for graduate jobs at the ...p employers is likely to be fiercer ...er...because not only are there ...acancies available but a record ...of new graduates will be leav-

almost a quarter fewer graduate jobs on offer next summer. John Lewis has suspended its programme altogether for the year while it reviews its future.

Law is down a more modest 2.1 per cent, while accountancy and professional services remain the largest graduate recruiters with 4,200 places on offer, up 1.8 per cent on last year. EY, the professional services company, will be taking on 850 graduates, down 50 on last year. The number of apprentice-...hips is up 50 to 250.

Brexit vote led to top firms cutting graduate recruitment

Richard Adams
Sally Weale

Uncertainty over Brexit...
of the UK's most presti...
ers to significantly cut...
recruitment, resulting...
number of new gradua...
first time since the fin...

A survey of the U...
graduate recruiters...

at large international organisations ...to reve... after a bumper year for

---

Fewer graduate jobs amid Brexit fears

Rosemary Bennett Education Editor

The number of jobs for graduates who left university last summer fell for the first time in five years as companies reined in their spending.

The country's biggest and best-...

are ever going to pay back the £54,000 a head they borrow to fund a degree.

They pay nothing until they earn £25,000 and outstanding debts are written off after 30 years. Recent estimates suggest that three quarters of graduates will not repay them in full,

cialist, suggest that the top 100 employers are optimistic about the year ahead, with graduate recruitment expected to recover by 3.6 per cent. Starting salaries at the UK's leading graduate employers are expected to remain unchanged for the fourth consecutive year at an

Understanding the Graduate Job Market

By **Martin Birchall**
Managing Director, High Fliers Research

When many of those graduating in the summer of 2019 arrived at university three years ago, the UK had just voted to leave the European Union and the big question for many was how it would affect the job market and graduates' career prospects.

The uncertainty that followed the Brexit vote meant that, for the first time in five years, the UK's leading employers cut their recruitment targets, and the number of graduates recruited fell in 2017.

Amidst the increasingly gloomy headlines, more than sixty of the employers featured in *The Times Top 100 Graduate Employers* recruited fewer graduates than the previous year, with the biggest cuts at the top City investment banks and other financial institutions, accounting and professional services firms, retailers and consulting firms.

In the two years since, graduate recruitment has rebounded and the number of vacancies for university-leavers increased by 4.3% in 2018 and by a further 9.9% in 2019. Many of the country's top graduate employers have tried to maintain a 'business as usual' approach to their annual recruitment and have continued to invest in their graduate development programmes.

When the global financial crisis struck a decade ago, the recession that followed in the UK in 2008 and 2009 had a much more dramatic effect on graduate vacancies and recruitment dropped by an unprecedented 23 per cent in less than eighteen months.

Although the graduate job market bounced back in 2010 with an annual increase in vacancies of more than 12 per cent, it took a further five years for graduate recruitment to overtake the pre-recession peak recorded in 2007.

By 2019, graduate recruitment was up by 43 per cent compared to the number of vacancies available in 2009 – the low-point in the graduate job market during the economic crisis. But even at this current level, graduate vacancies are still just 10 per cent higher than then were twelve years ago.

For many employers, the recovery from the recession was neither uniform nor straightforward, and graduate vacancies in seven key sectors – oil & energy, the City's investment banks, law firms, media organisations, financial services, and the Armed Forces – all remain lower than they were in 2007.

So what is the outlook for final year students graduating from university in 2020? The initial recruitment targets published by the employers featured in this edition of The Times Top 100 Graduate Employers suggest that the number of vacancies available will be very similar to 2019.

> *Public sector employers featured in the latest Top 100 rankings are set to recruit more graduates than any other sector in 2020.*

Although a third of *Top 100* employers are planning to expand their graduate intake in 2020 and a further third expect to take on the same number of new recruits in the next 12 months, thirty-one organisations warn that they will be hiring fewer graduates than in 2019. Together, the employers appearing in this year's *Top 100* are advertising 24,625 vacancies for 2020, compared to the 24,859 graduates hired in 2019 – an annual decrease of 0.9 per cent.

The eleven government departments and other public sector employers featured in the latest *Top 100* rankings are set to recruit more graduates than any other sector in 2020. With vacancies for over 5,200 new graduates, this will be the biggest-ever graduate intake for the public sector, and the eighth time in the last ten years that its graduate recruitment has increased.

The UK's leading accountancy & professional services firms are also planning to recruit over 5,000 new trainees in 2020, equating to more than a fifth of the total number of graduate vacancies available at the *Top 100* employers.

Overall, employers in ten of the fifteen industries and business sectors represented within the *Top 100* expect to maintain or increase their graduate

recruitment in 2020, but there will be fewer entry-level vacancies at the major technology companies, consulting firms, law firms, chemical & pharmaceuticals companies, and three of the 'Big Four' accounting & professional services firms.

For the second year running, the organisation with the largest graduate recruitment target within *The Times Top 100 Graduate Employers* is Teach First. The popular programme that recruits new graduates to teach in schools in low income communities around the UK has 1,750 places available in 2020.

Other substantial individual graduate recruiters include the accounting & professional services firms PwC (1,350 graduate vacancies), KPMG (1,200 vacancies) and Deloitte (1,000 vacancies), the Civil Service Fast Stream (1,200 vacancies), HSBC (1,000 vacancies) and Enterprise Rent-A-Car (900 vacancies).

Half the employers featured in this year's *Top 100* have vacancies for graduates in technology, two-fifths have opportunities in finance, and a third are recruiting for engineering positions, human resources roles or general management jobs. Up to a quarter of employers are looking for recruits to work in marketing, research & development

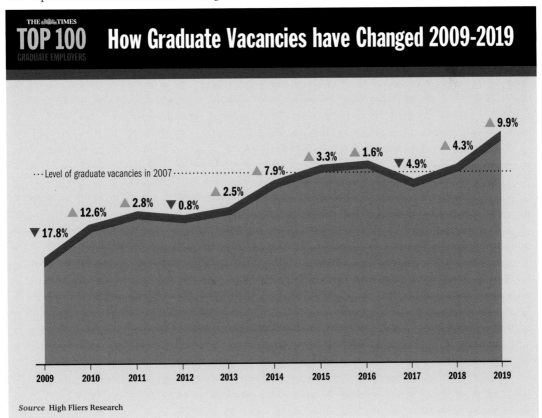

THE TIMES
TOP 100 **How Graduate Vacancies have Changed 2009-2019**
GRADUATE EMPLOYERS

▲ 9.9%

▲ 4.3%

▲ 3.3% ▲ 1.6% ▼ 4.9%

····Level of graduate vacancies in 2007······················ ▲ 7.9%

▲ 2.5%

▲ 2.8% ▼ 0.8%

▲ 12.6%

▼ 17.8%

2009 2010 2011 2012 2013 2014 2015 2016 2017 2018 2019

Source High Fliers Research

or sales, but there are fewer opportunities in retail and more specialist areas such as logistics, purchasing, property and the media.

More than eighty *Top 100* employers have graduate vacancies in London in 2018, and half have posts available elsewhere in the south east of England. Up to half also have graduate roles in the north west of England, the Midlands and the south west. Northern Ireland, Wales, East Anglia and the north east of England have the fewest employers with graduate vacancies.

Graduate starting salaries at the UK's leading employers have hardly changed over the last nine years. After annual increases every year up to 2010, the average salary on offer from the country's top employers remained at £29,000 for four consecutive years, before increasing again in 2014 and 2015. The average graduate starting salary in 2019 was £30,000 for the fifth year running.

More than half of the organisations featured in this year's edition of *The Times Top 100 Graduate Employers* have opted to leave their graduate starting salaries unchanged for 2020 but a limited number of employers have announced increases to their graduate pay packages – typically between £500 and £2,000.

The most generous graduate salary publicised within this edition of the *Top 100* is at Newton, the consulting firm, which is offering graduate

packages of up to £50,000 in 2020, plus a starting-work bonus. Leading law firms Clifford Chance, White & Case and Baker McKenzie are set to pay their new trainees salaries of £48,000, whilst a further five legal firms now offer starting salaries of between £45,000 and £47,000.

Technology company TPP pays its new recruits £45,000, and the retailer Aldi continues to offer a sector-leading graduate starting salary of £44,000, plus a fully-expensed company car.

Up to half of the UK's leading employers now recruit graduates year-round, or in different phases during the year, and will accept applications throughout the 2019-2020 recruitment season until all their vacancies are filled.

For employers with a set application deadline, most are in either November or December, although a limited number of organisations have October or post-Christmas deadlines for their graduate programmes.

Three-fifths of *Top 100* employers insist that applicants for their graduate schemes should have a 2.1 degree or better, and a fifth specify a minimum UCAS tariff too, mostly in the range of 'ABB' to 'BCC' grades at A-level.

So, for those who make the grade, there is a wide range of career opportunities and some excellent starting salaries on offer from *The Times Top 100 Graduate Employers* in 2020.

THE TIMES TOP 100 GRADUATE EMPLOYERS
Graduate Vacancies at Top 100 Employers in 2020

	2019		NUMBER OF VACANCIES IN 2020	CHANGE SINCE 2019	MEDIAN STARTING SALARY IN 2019
1.	2	PUBLIC SECTOR EMPLOYERS	5,222	▲ 0.8%	£24,000
2.	1	ACCOUNTANCY & PROFESSIONAL SERVICES FIRMS	5,205	▼ 6.4%	£31,200
3.	3	ENGINEERING & INDUSTRIAL COMPANIES	2,348	▲ 5.1%	£28,000
4.	5	BANKING & FINANCIAL SERVICES	2,120	▲ 5.7%	£32,500
5.	6	INVESTMENT BANKS & FUND MANAGERS	1,815	▲ 4.1%	£50,000
6.	4	TECHNOLOGY COMPANIES	1,814	▼ 14.4%	£31,500
7.	7	ARMED FORCES	1,550	▲ 1.0%	£26,500
8.	9	MEDIA ORGANISATIONS	1,014	▲ 13.7%	£30,500
9.	8	LAW FIRMS	926	▼ 6.1%	£45,000
10.	10	RETAILERS	800	NO CHANGE	£33,000
11.	11	CONSULTING FIRMS	230	▼ 4.2%	£45,000
12.	12	CONSUMER GOODS MANUFACTURERS	201	▲ 5.2%	£32,000
13.	13	OIL & ENERGY COMPANIES	170	▲ 3.0%	£38,500
14.	14	CHARITY & VOLUNTARY SECTOR EMPLOYERS	162	NO CHANGE	£26,000
15.	15	CHEMICAL & PHARMACEUTICAL COMPANIES	148	▼ 1.3%	£29,300

Source High Fliers Research

GET THE SKILLS TO LEAD AND SUCCEED.

THE BMW GROUP UK GRADUATE PROGRAMME AND THE GLOBAL LEADER DEVELOPMENT PROGRAMME.

Those who want to lead can learn it here, step by step, with a global leader driven by passion for innovative mobility solutions.

If you share our passion, enjoy taking on responsibilities and want to lay the foundation for a rewarding and successful career, join us on our 24-month Graduate Programme or our Global Leader Development Programme.

Apply now at www.bmwgroup.jobs/uk

Use your degree to inspire the next generation.

Teaching is a chance to inspire the next generation and **make a real difference** in children's lives.

The average starting salary for new graduates is **£23,000**.* Newly-qualified teachers for 2018/2019 had a starting salary of **£29,664** in inner London and at least **£23,720** outside London. As you progress into leadership roles, so will your salary. Teachers in leadership roles earn **£58,881** on average.

To support your year of training, the Government provide **tax-free bursaries**[†] for new graduates. Those who started their teacher training in 2019 received up to £26,000.

Postgraduate teacher training courses are available across England, led by universities or schools. Whichever course you choose, your training will largely be the same, and will usually offer a **postgraduate qualification** like a PGCE.

Search: **Get Into Teaching**

Charlie Yeates, history teacher

Jo Richardson Community School

Department for Education

"I decided to become a teacher because I had a real love of history and loved sharing what I had learnt with other people. However, I wouldn't have pursued it as a career had it not been for the enthusiastic History teachers who I encountered during my time as a student.

Growing up in Dagenham, I saw the real impact of what good teachers could do for students, especially those who could easily have followed the wrong path. I wanted to help create a positive environment.

Not only am I now working in the region I grew up in, but the school I was taught at – so I'm constantly reminded of the personal experiences that shaped me.

Teacher training has made me a more responsible, organised and understanding person in general. Before teacher training, I didn't have much direction, my days didn't have a general structure, and I had no responsibility. However, now I see direction in what I'm doing, as well as a purpose, which has been a great motivator in terms of doing well in my personal life too.

The myth is that teachers are less social due to their workload, but personally I've become much more social with old friends, and also with the people I'm working with. Overall, being a teacher has contributed massively to a greater happiness in my life."

Teaching ✓

Every Lesson Shapes a Life

Successful Graduate Job Hunting

By **Stuart Johnson**
Director of Careers Service, University of Bristol

On average, the employers featured in this edition of *The Times Top 100 Graduate Employers* had thirty-eight applications per graduate vacancy in 2019, which means they rejected over 97% of those who applied to them.

One of the main drivers for making a successful application is whether you actually want the job, internship or work placement that you're applying for. Your application, and what you do in the subsequent recruitment process, has to convince the employer that not only do you have the skills and experiences they're looking for, but you genuinely want to work for them, in that specific role.

It isn't going to be enough to say that you're interested in a graduate job in sales or an internship in finance, you have to be able to articulate exactly why you're interested in sales at this specific consumer goods company or the internship at that particular high-street bank.

A big part of this involves carrying out some thorough research. There are plenty of opportunities on campuses across the country to meet graduate employers and build up your own picture of them and the jobs they're offering. Whether it's a careers fair, an employer's own recruitment presentation, a pop-up promotional event or a skills workshop, you'll have the chance to speak to recruiters and recent graduates who

"Simply saying, 'I've always wanted to work for you', without explaining why, isn't going to work, however much you think you mean it. "

work for the employer, to find out first-hand what they're offering and what their jobs are really like.

You can, of course, just have a free cup of coffee or a glass of wine and chat to them casually, but we'd always encourage you to take these events more seriously. For example, at a careers fair, don't waste your time – and theirs – by asking employers 'what do you do' or asking things they answer on page one of their recruitment website. Try and use the time to have real conversations about the employer's culture, what it takes to do well there, and if their current graduates enjoy their jobs.

Most employers have their own online application systems, but it's always helpful to put together your CV before you start making applications. Whether that's as a traditional Word-style document or your profile on *LinkedIn*, it will be a useful aide-memoire and a reminder of the things you've done at school and university, and the skills and experience you've developed.

You can then use that as the basis for your applications and spend your time tailoring each one to the individual employer and the role you're applying for, so that every application is as convincing and compelling as it can be.

The style and content of employers' application processes do vary considerably. Some are effectively little more than a registration process,

but many will ask competency- or strength-based questions, like 'describe a time when you led a team successfully' or 'when did you achieve something you're really proud of?', as well as 'why are you applying for this role?'. These types of question need careful preparation and will require both time and quite a bit of thought to complete well.

The other thing to bear in mind is when to make your applications. Some employers have annual recruiting cycles for their graduate programmes, with a single application deadline, often in November or December. Others open applications as early as June or July for the following year's entry, but then close them once they've filled their places. And some recruit year-round, both before and after graduation. For 'taster' weeks, course placements and internships, the deadlines are often quite different to those for graduate programmes. It's crucial, therefore, to start your applications as early as possible and prioritise them so you don't miss out on an employer that you're interested in. This is no different from managing your academic deadlines, whether that's knowing when your next essay is due or planning a big final year project.

Your university careers service can help you through each of these stages, whether it's finding out about which employers are visiting your university, exploring the kind of jobs that you might be suited to, preparing applications, or supporting you through the selection process.

There's no magic number of applications that you need to make in order to secure a job offer, but it's always better to do fewer higher quality applications than lots of rushed, lower quality applications. If a student comes to us and says: 'I've made fifty applications and nobody's got back to me', our advice would always be to come and see us before it gets to that situation. Trying a different approach earlier could save a great deal of frustration and rejections.

Once you've submitted your application to an employer, the next stage is often some form of online testing. It's becoming the norm that employers test every applicant for things like numeracy, verbal reasoning, problem solving and their situational judgement, rather than relying on academic results or your predicted degree. Your careers service can help you practice these beforehand because it's unlikely you'll have done anything similar whilst you've been at university.

The next challenge after these online tests is likely to be a first-round interview. This is sometimes done over the phone, but increasingly employers are using recorded online video interviews. Although these automated interviews can seem a bit strange, the benefit for both employer and student is that these are asynchronous experiences that can be done whenever the student chooses. And the

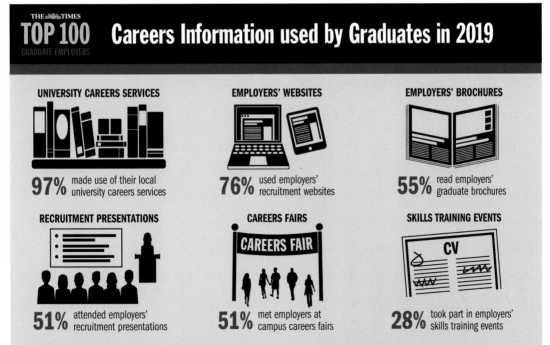

THE TIMES TOP 100 GRADUATE EMPLOYERS — Careers Information used by Graduates in 2019

UNIVERSITY CAREERS SERVICES
97% made use of their local university careers services

EMPLOYERS' WEBSITES
76% used employers' recruitment websites

EMPLOYERS' BROCHURES
55% read employers' graduate brochures

RECRUITMENT PRESENTATIONS
51% attended employers' recruitment presentations

CAREERS FAIRS
51% met employers at campus careers fairs

SKILLS TRAINING EVENTS
28% took part in employers' skills training events

Source **High Fliers Research** 19,712 final year students leaving UK universities in the summer of 2019 were asked which careers resources and information they had used whilst researching graduate employers, during interviews for *The UK Graduate Careers Survey 2019*

Join an AstraZeneca Graduate Programme and help push the boundaries of science to deliver life-changing medicines

At AstraZeneca we believe in the potential of our people and you'll develop beyond what you thought possible. We make the most of your skills and passion by actively supporting you to see what you can achieve on our Global Graduate Programmes.

results can be viewed – or in some cases analysed by AI – at a convenient point for the employer.

Before attempting a video interview, think through where you are going to do it. Find a place where you won't be interrupted, which doesn't have a distracting backdrop. You don't need to put on a suit, but equally a T-shirt and shorts may not create the right impression either. The key thing is that you should feel as confident as possible in yourself.

Again, preparation and practice will make all the difference here. You may need to draw on some of the answers you gave to the free-text questions on your original application form, such as your experiences of teamwork, leadership or problem-solving. Employers aren't expecting you to be a TV news presenter, but neither do you want to be constantly reading from a sheet of notes.

For the last part of the selection process, the style of assessment changes. Whereas previously it's been you as an individual versus the process, at a final-round assessment centre it's you alongside other shortlisted candidates. That makes it clear that you are now interacting with as well as competing against others, and that the employer is keen to see how you do both.

It's very important, therefore, that you think about how you're going to come across on the day. If it's just about you and getting your point across,

and you're in a competition and want to win, that's probably going to backfire.

You should be greatly encouraged to have got this far because the employer wouldn't have selected you for the assessment centre if they didn't think you were capable and suitable for the job. They've seen that you have potential and want you to perform well.

The day will include face-to-face interviews and group exercises, sometimes with more tests, a presentation or problem-solving. For the group experiences, remember not to talk over everybody else. But equally, if you don't say anything at all, you're going to struggle too because the employer is keen to see how you interact in a team situation.

It's essential to prepare for the interviews by thinking through the points you want to get across beforehand, including your all-important answer as to why you want this particular job, at this organisation. In order to be genuinely convincing, this needs to be backed up by the research you've done. Simply saying, 'I've always wanted to work for you', without explaining why, isn't going to work, however much you think you mean it.

There's a lot to do, but by planning ahead and breaking it down into the constituent parts, it becomes much more manageable – and ultimately more successful.

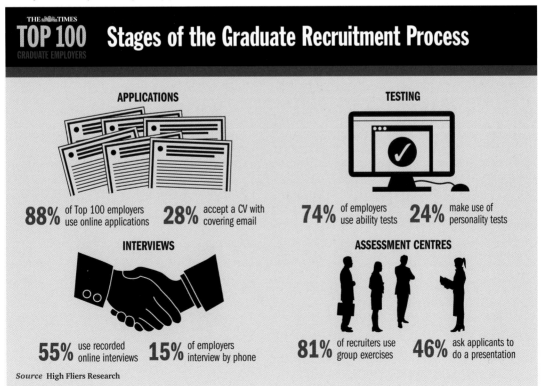

THE TIMES TOP 100 GRADUATE EMPLOYERS
Stages of the Graduate Recruitment Process

APPLICATIONS

88% of Top 100 employers use online applications
28% accept a CV with covering email

TESTING

74% of employers use ability tests
24% make use of personality tests

INTERVIEWS

55% use recorded online interviews
15% of employers interview by phone

ASSESSMENT CENTRES

81% of recruiters use group exercises
46% ask applicants to do a presentation

Source High Fliers Research

Deloitte.

Where are solutions before they're found?

Welcome to the home of the curious.
A place for those who know that imagination,
ingenuity and solution finding are what
humans are made of. We offer life-changing
careers and professional qualifications,
across all industries, to those who are true
to themselves. Those who set no limits to
their dreams and ambitions.

deloitte.co.uk/careers
What impact will you make?

We eat impossible
for breakfast.

Drones that deliver phone signal.
A sensor that predicts when baby cows are born.

Working at Vodafone means working on projects that are truly extraordinary.
We need outstanding graduates to achieve our ambitious goals. Join us, get hands-on
experience across a huge range of specialities, and build a remarkable career.

Discover our graduate opportunities –
careers.vodafone.com

The future is exciting.

Ready?

Getting Ready for the Working World

By **Carol Lewis**
Deputy Personal Finance & Property Editor, The Times

After three or four years at university, you may be used to living away from home, have learnt how to juggle your student finances, and might even have got the hang of cooking and ironing. But moving on from university and starting your first job with an employer like those featured in *The Times Top 100 Graduate Employers* will bring a whole set of new challenges.

As soon as you secure your new job you will need to find somewhere to live, and for most people this will mean looking for rental accommodation.

If you're about to head off to a new city, then it makes sense to rent in a shared house or a co-living block where you can meet other people and give your social life a kick start. There are websites, such as *SpareRoom*, *Ideal Flatmate* and *RoomGo*, that advertise spare rooms in shared houses and help match you with suitable people. Of course, it's important to go and see the room in person and meet your prospective flatmates, rather than relying solely on online descriptions.

A more expensive option is co-living in an apartment block, where everyone lives in a studio or small apartment and shares communal facilities. For instance, The Collective, a London- and New York-based co-living developer, has apartments and rooms with ensuite bathrooms and shared kitchens from £1,083 a month in its co-living block near Willesden Junction in West London. The monthly rent includes all bills, 24-hour concierge, cleaner, cinema room, gym membership, co-working spaces, roof terrace and an events programme. There is also a restaurant and bar on site. YPP offers similar properties and services in the north of England.

If you're renting a flat or house to share with friends, striking a deal directly with the landlord – rather than going via a lettings agent – could save you money. Websites such as *HomeRenter* and *OpenRent* match landlords and tenants. However, it's worth remembering that agents can be good as they should act quickly if there is a problem and repairs or maintenance are needed.

Inevitably, when you start work, your accommodation will be your single biggest expense. According to estate agents Hamptons International, the average cost of renting a property in Greater London is now £1,737 per month, compared to £1,078 elsewhere in the south east, £631 in the north of England, £821 in the west, £655 in Scotland and £668 in Wales. Room rents in flatshares now average £724 in London, compared to £571 elsewhere.

On top of that, whether you're renting a room in a shared house or are planning to have a penthouse all to yourself, you're likely to need to

> *« Eye-watering interest rates mean that graduates are likely to make student loan repayments for up to thirty years after graduation. »*

We eat impossible for breakfast.

**Drones that deliver phone signal.
A sensor that predicts when baby cows are born.**

Working at Vodafone means working on projects that are truly extraordinary.
We need outstanding graduates to achieve our ambitious goals. Join us, get hands-on
experience across a huge range of specialities, and build a remarkable career.

Discover our graduate opportunities –
careers.vodafone.com

The future is exciting.
Ready?

pay a refundable deposit of up to six weeks' rent and often a refundable holding deposit to reserve the property too. These are substantial costs and are payable before you move in.

The Mayor of London, Sadiq Khan, has urged employers to do more to help by offering loans to cover rental deposits, preferential lending terms for mortgages, and even providing their own rental accommodation for staff. A number of employers ranked in this year's edition of *The Times Top 100 Graduate Employers*, including Deloitte, Arup, Morgan Stanley, Pinsent Masons and Grant Thornton have signed up to the campaign, so it's worthwhile checking what help your future employer can offer. At the very least they might have a website where staff advertise for flatshares. Some companies also offer relocation allowances to help with moving, or salary advances to help cover initial moving costs.

Few graduates are in the fortunate position to be able to buy their own property straight after university. The average age of a first-time homebuyer has increased from 25 to 33 years old in the last two decades, and 40 per cent will have already started a family by the time they get the keys to their first home.

The biggest barrier to buying your own house or flat is saving for the deposit, a process that can take years. And while cutting down on lattes, avocados and other day-to-day living costs is often suggested as a way to save for your deposit, it's worth noting that to save the average deposit of £21,966 needed for a property in the UK, you would have to skip 8,966 lattes or 21,749 avocados, according to research by the *ReallyMoving* website. And to save enough for the average deposit in London, which is a staggering £40,945, you would need to forgo 15,590 lattes or 37,817 avocados.

When you're choosing where to live, it's also important to consider your daily commute to work. Although homes near good transport connections often cost more to rent, it could work out more cost effective than an expensive season ticket. The Campaign for Better Transport have calculated that some commuters now spend a fifth of their take-home pay on commuting to work. You also need to consider your sanity, because a long commute and dependence on an unreliable train line could adversely affect your quality of life.

Some employers will offer support, with a low-interest or interest-free loan to help you buy a season ticket. Getting an annual ticket is always more cost effective than monthly ones. For instance, the *Money Saving Expert* website calculated that a commuter travelling from Guildford to Tottenham Court Road in central London could save £702.40 a year if they bought an annual ticket rather than twelve monthly ones.

If you need a car to get to and from work, then there are several options. The most popular are car leasing and personal contract plans, where you pay a deposit and then regular monthly payments for about three years, before giving the car back. Alternatively, you can opt for hire-purchase, in which you pay a deposit and then monthly instalments until you have bought the car.

But if you simply need a car occasionally for an hour or two outside of work, consider joining a car club like Zipcar, in which you pay a monthly membership fee in return for access to cars parked on local streets. A typical package has a monthly charge of £6 with loan charges of £6 per hour.

As you leave university, your bank account is likely to switch automatically from a student account to a graduate account. But loyalty rarely pays when it comes to banking, so shop around for the best deals and use the Current Account Switch Service to ensure all your direct debits move with the account. You'll be eligible for a graduate account for up to three years after graduation, so when choosing a new account look for an interest-free overdraft and, if possible, interest rates on positive balances or cashback on your spending.

It may also be worth considering some of the new so-called 'challenger' banks, such as Monzo and Starling, as these offer app-driven accounts, immediate notifications on expenditure, budget 'pots' to help you save, and cost-effective ATM and currency conversion when you're abroad.

Another major consideration for your personal finances after university will be your student loans. Data from *The UK Graduate Careers Survey 2019*, produced by High Fliers Research, shows the average debt for graduates leaving the UK's top universities in the summer of 2019 was £40,300, much of which was made up of tuition fee loans and maintenance loans. These loans are repayable from the April following your graduation if you're earning above £25,725, and your employer will deduct 9 per cent of whatever you earn above this level on behalf of the Student Loans Company.

The interest charged on your tuition fee loans and maintenance loans depends on the Retail Price Index (RPI) – which was 2.9 per cent as of June

2019 – and how much you earn as a graduate. For those earning £25,725 or less, the interest will be equal to RPI, but between £25,725 and £46,305 this rises to RPI plus up to a maximum of 3 per cent, on a sliding scale based on your salary. These eye-watering interest rates mean that most graduates are likely to continue to make student loan repayments for up to thirty years after graduation.

As well as paying off debts, you will need to hand over some of your hard-earned cash to the tax office in the form of income tax and National Insurance (NI). When you first start work, you need to tell your employer your NI number to make sure the income tax and NI you pay are properly recorded. You will find your number on the card or notification letter you received from HM Revenue & Customs when you turned sixteen.

HMRC will issue a PAYE (pay as you earn) code to your employer which tells them how much tax to take from your income, and they will also send you a copy with details of how it has been calculated. You don't pay tax on everything you earn. Up to £12,500 is tax-free, then from £12,501 to £50,000 income tax is charged at 20 per cent. After this it rises to 40 per cent and then above £150,000 it hits 45 per cent. You will also pay National Insurance

of 12 per cent on your earnings between £8,500 and £50,000, and 2 per cent thereafter.

You'll also notice that money will be deducted by your employer to go towards a pension. New rules mean that every employee is now automatically included in a company pension scheme. This means you pay in 4 per cent of your earnings, your employer pays the equivalent of a further 3 per cent, and the government adds in a further 1 per cent in tax relief, giving you a total contribution of 8 per cent of your salary.

Finally, if you have anything left after paying tax, student loans and pensions, you might want to start saving towards a house deposit. The best way to do this is by opening a Lifetime Individual Savings Account (LISA), which will enable you to save up to £4,000 a year until you are aged 50. The government will add a bonus of 25 per cent to your savings, up to £1,000 a year. You can withdraw the money when you buy your first home or when you are aged 60 to use as a retirement pension.

But retirement can wait for now. Once you leave university, it's all about enjoying your first few weeks and months in employment, settling into your new job, and making the most of life as a graduate.

Understanding the Cost of Living for New Graduates

CASE STUDY A *Will graduated last year from the University of Leeds with a 2.1 in Computer Science. He's now working as a software engineer at the BBC in MediaCityUK with an annual salary of £24,000, and is sharing a one-bedroom apartment with his partner in nearby Salford. He is currently cycling to work.*

MONTHLY STATEMENT	
Gross Income	**£2,000.00**
Income tax	-£179.76
National Insurance	-£153.68
Pension deduction (4%)	-£59.55
Student Loan repayment	-£0.00
Take-Home Pay	**£1,607.01**
Share of apartment rent	-£350.00
Share of council tax	-£60.00
Share of bills (gas, electric, broadband)	-£65.94
Mobile phone contract	-£45.60
Cycling to work	-£0.00
Groceries	-£150.00
Disposable Income	**£935.47**

CASE STUDY B *Hannah left the University of Exeter with a 1st in Ancient History and is now a tax trainee at one of the 'Big Four' accounting & professional services firms in central London, earning a salary of £30,000. She's renting a room in a shared house in Wembley and commutes to work on the London Underground.*

MONTHLY STATEMENT	
Gross Income	**£2,500.00**
Income tax	-£275.76
National Insurance	-£213.68
Pension deduction (4%)	-£79.55
Student Loan repayment	-£32.06
Take-Home Pay	**£1,898.95**
Room rent (inc. council tax & bills)	-£750.00
Mobile phone contract	-£45.60
Monthly Travelcard (Zones 1-4)	-£194.00
Groceries	-£180.00
Disposable Income	**£729.35**

Sources www.thesalarycalculator.co.uk, www.moneyadviceservice.org.uk, www.rightmove.co.uk, www.spareroom.co.uk, tfl.gov.uk

SHAPE YOUR FUTURE

40% of our board joined us as graduates

Do you have what it takes?

Become the future of Savills

savills.com/graduate

🐦 @savillsgraduate

📷 savills_instagrad

THE TIMES
GRADUATE RECRUITMENT
AWARDS 2019
'Graduate Employer of Choice'
PROPERTY

savills

Give it everything.

We'll give you more.

Graduate Area Manager Programme
- **£44,000 starting salary (rising to £76,495 after four years)**
- **Pension • Healthcare • Audi A4/BMW 3 series**
- **All-year round recruitment but places fill quickly**

aldirecruitment.co.uk/graduates

sTudent?

Stand out from the crowd with a subscription to The Times and The Sunday Times

As part of your subscription, you can enjoy:

Times+
Subscribers get access to events, discounts and deals, such as cinema tickets and more.

Reliable reporting
Where most papers rush, we collate and consider. Get more expert analysis and in-depth opinion.

Exclusive content
Access inspiring guides, videos and podcasts released throughout the year.

Save 92% on your subscription with full digital access for just 50p a week.

Purchase your subscription to start taking advantage of these benefits and many more. Visit thetimes.co.uk

THE TIMES
THE SUNDAY TIMES
Know your times

THE TIMES
TOP 100
GRADUATE EMPLOYERS

Sector Guide to the UK's Top Graduate Employers

1999-2019

The 'Big Four' firms – Deloitte, EY, KPMG and PwC – have long dominated the accounting & professional services sector, and together they audit the accounts of 243 of the UK's 250 largest companies.

All four firms have appeared in every edition of *The Times Top 100 Graduate Employers* over the last two decades, and in nine out of the last ten years each of the four firms have been ranked within the top ten graduate employers.

In an unparalleled achievement, the sector's leading employer, PwC, was rated the UK's number one graduate employer in the *Top 100* for an impressive 15 consecutive years until 2018, and the firm continues to be the 'graduate employer of choice' for accounting & professional services in the latest rankings.

For Andrew Bargery, Campus & Schools Engagement Leader in Student Recruitment at PwC, much of the firm's enduring appeal is based on the quality of the training and development that it offers.

"We provide highly structured training for all of our graduates, and most have the opportunity to become a chartered accountant or train for another professional qualification in their first two or three years with the firm," he explains. "Our training and development is second to none, so having PwC on your CV gives you a flying start to your career, but having a chartered accountancy qualification is transferable across so many different roles in business."

PwC recruits up to 1,400 graduate trainees and over 600 undergraduate placement students each year and works hard to promote its entry-level programmes at UK universities.

"We typically recruit new graduates from around a hundred

Andrew Bargery, Campus & Schools Engagement Leader, Student Recruitment, PwC

UK universities and visit the majority of these during the annual recruitment round," enthuses Bargery. "Last year we hosted almost 700 individual campus events and promotions to help students in all years of study understand the culture of the firm, the opportunities available, and meet our people."

It's a crucial part of the firm's recruitment strategy, particularly as PwC now recruits graduates for roles in eight different areas of the firm, with a total of more than 25 individual programmes on offer.

"We are seen first and foremost as an accountancy firm, but fewer than half of this year's graduate trainees joined our audit practice," Bargery says. "We're now recruiting more graduates than ever to work in consulting and technology, tackling clients' problems with issues like sustainability and climate change or cyber security and big data."

The firm hires graduates to work in each of its 24 offices across the UK, and approximately 60% of its vacancies are outside of London.

"We talk in our marketing about PwC being the opportunity of a lifetime and a big part of that is the range of experiences that the firm can offer with high-profile clients across the country," reflects Bargery. "You can join the firm as an accountancy trainee and then move into other areas like corporate finance, consulting or technology. We really are training graduates to become the business leaders of the future."

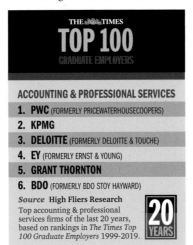

THE TIMES
TOP 100
GRADUATE EMPLOYERS

ACCOUNTING & PROFESSIONAL SERVICES

1. **PWC** (FORMERLY PRICEWATERHOUSECOOPERS)
2. **KPMG**
3. **DELOITTE** (FORMERLY DELOITTE & TOUCHE)
4. **EY** (FORMERLY ERNST & YOUNG)
5. **GRANT THORNTON**
6. **BDO** (FORMERLY BDO STOY HAYWARD)

Source **High Fliers Research**
Top accounting & professional services firms of the last 20 years, based on rankings in *The Times Top 100 Graduate Employers* 1999-2019.

We value your dedication.
Because we're just as dedicated.

At HSBC we like our employees to focus on doing the right thing – to strive forward and reach for new heights. Because it's this sense of purpose and dedication that enables us to best serve all our customers.

That's why we're looking for people who think, see and do things differently. Regardless of your degree discipline, we have a variety of internship and graduate opportunities just for you.

Visit hsbc.com/earlycareers

 HSBC

Together we thrive

Sector Guide to the UK's Top Graduate Employers 1999-2019

Banking & Finance

A dozen of the UK's best-known banking groups, insurance companies and financial institutions have appeared in *The Times Top 100 Graduate Employers* over the last two decades. HSBC, Barclays and Lloyds Banking Group have each been ranked amongst the country's leading graduate employers every year since 1999.

RBS, which includes brands like The Royal Bank of Scotland, NatWest, Ulster Bank and Coutts, achieved a place in the top twenty employers for five years between 2004 and 2008, and has climbed the rankings for the fourth year running in 2019.

"RBS is very proud of the real commitment that we've made over the last few years to create a great place to work across the whole bank, not just for our graduate population," says Sandra Beattie, Talent Acquisition Lead, Early Career and Contingent Labour at RBS. "We've worked very hard to keep people – both our customers and colleagues – at the absolute heart of everything that we do."

The bank recruits around 250 graduates annually for its 14 entry-level programmes including software engineering, risk, customer solutions, data & analytics and HR.

"We've built an innovative game called 'Find Your Path' that we encourage students to play before they apply," explains Beattie. "It's designed to help applicants understand which of our programmes they would be most suited to and where they could fit within RBS. Each programme offers a dedicated learning journey that ensures every graduate gets exposure to roles in different parts of the bank, and to our customers."

The bank also offers over 150 ten-week internships each summer

Sandra Beattie, Talent Acquisition Lead, Early Career & Contingent Labour, RBS

for penultimate year students, and typically 85% of these are offered a graduate position with RBS after university.

RBS is currently the only employer in *The Times Top 100 Graduate Employers* to be headquartered in Scotland. Half of its new graduates are based at the bank's 120-acre head office campus in Gogarburn on the outskirts of Edinburgh. More than 6,000 RBS staff work at

Gogarburn, which boasts its own business school, a start-up hub for entrepreneurs, a leisure centre and a 10km running track.

"The campus is a big selling point for our graduates and interns because of its fantastic facilities and being so close to the city of Edinburgh," says Beattie. "And elsewhere in the UK, like lots of banks, we've changed our footprint in London and are now starting to create many more graduate roles in Edinburgh, as well as in Birmingham, Manchester and Bristol."

Previous experience of banking or finance is not a prerequisite for any of RBS's graduate programmes or internships. And, with the exception of the software engineering programme, nor is a relevant degree subject.

In spite of all the continuing uncertainties over Brexit, RBS remains firmly committed to its graduate recruitment. "Our graduate intake for 2020 has been officially signed off," assures Beattie. "Demand for new talent is up year-on-year, so there'll be a 10% increase in our graduate hires next year."

THE TIMES
TOP 100
GRADUATE EMPLOYERS

BANKING & FINANCE

1. HSBC
2. BARCLAYS
3. RBS (FORMERLY ROYAL BANK OF SCOTLAND, NATWEST)
4. LLOYDS BANKING GROUP
5. SANTANDER (FORMERLY ABBEY NATIONAL)
6. BANK OF ENGLAND
7. CAPITAL ONE
8. LLOYD'S
9. FINANCIAL SERVICES AUTHORITY
10. NATIONWIDE

Source High Fliers Research
Top banking & finance employers of the last 20 years, based on their annual rankings in *The Times Top 100 Graduate Employers* 1999-2019.

We only recruit one type of person

FEMALEBLACKMALEASIAN SCHOOLLEAVERUNIVERSITY GRADUATEDISABLEDGAY BRITISHCITIZEN

You might think there's an MI5 'type'. **Think again.**
We need people who can bring a rich mix of skills,
experiences and backgrounds to help us fight the
threats we face. Our differences make us stronger.
Together, we help to keep the country safe.

To find out more, please visit www.mi5.gov.uk/careers

"Proud winners at the British LGBT Awards 2018"

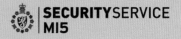

Consulting

For the last five years, consulting has been the number one career destination for the UK's top graduates, and record numbers of final year students from the 'Class of 2019' applied for entry-level jobs in the sector.

A total of twelve consulting firms have been listed in the *The Times Top 100 Graduate Employers* over the last two decades, but just one, McKinsey & Company, has been ranked every year since 1999.

In the 2019 rankings, the leading employer in the sector is Newton, a firm that only launched in 2001. It appeared as a new entry in the *Top 100* six years ago and is now one of the UK's top 20 graduate recruiters.

According to Samantha Knollys, a Director at the firm, Newton takes a different approach to consulting than many of the more traditional firms.

"When people think of consulting, they tend to think of people who go into a business, analyse a problem, tell the business what to do and write a report," she explains. "What makes us very different is that we do hands-on implementation. We work with fewer clients over a much longer time period, where we go in and diagnose their issues and then actually work with their frontline teams to implement operational and cultural change and achieve real results for them."

This business model means that the firm is paid differently too. "We believe so strongly in what we can achieve together, that we guarantee our fees against delivering results," Knollys says. "It means everyone's very focused and committed, and passionate about getting results."

Newton currently has around 300 employees and is looking to recruit up to 100 graduates in 2020.

Samantha Knollys, Director, Newton

"It's a demanding role and, with clients all over the country, our graduates do need to be prepared to travel and live away from home at times," Knollys acknowledges. "But wherever they're working, everyone must be home by 6pm on a Friday and nobody works weekends."

This emphasis on welfare and support is a key part of Newton's culture. "Because our consultants aren't office-based, every two weeks on a Friday, we get the entire business together for a review day," she continues. "It's been running for as long as the firm has been running and is a great way to get everyone talking, getting input and advice from others who are working with different clients. It puts a focus on developing people, teamwork and having fun together, which is quite unique."

Graduates joining Newton receive a salary package worth £45,000-£50,000, including a joining bonus and a car allowance.

"We're looking for very high performers with the right values, who'll fit with the culture of the firm," explains Knollys. "But one of the most attractive things about Newton is the speed that graduates can progress. By the third week, they're out with a client, doing analysis and frontline work. And you don't have to wait a year for a promotion, there's the opportunity to be promoted on merit every fortnight."

THE TIMES
TOP 100
GRADUATE EMPLOYERS

CONSULTING

1. MCKINSEY & COMPANY
2. BAIN & COMPANY
3. BOSTON CONSULTING GROUP
4. NEWTON
5. METASWITCH NETWORKS
6. PA CONSULTING
7. MERCER
8. OLIVER WYMAN
9. MARAKON ASSOCIATES
10. MITCHELL MADISON GROUP

Source High Fliers Research
Top consulting firms of the last 20 years, based on their annual rankings in *The Times Top 100 Graduate Employers* 1999-2019.

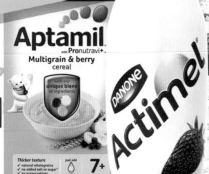

Consumer Goods

Whilst their company names may not always be the most familiar, the brands produced by the top consumer goods manufacturers are known the world over.

Unilever, P&G, L'Oréal and Mars have each been listed in *The Times Top 100 Graduate Employers* every year since its launch in 1999, and a further eleven employers from the consumer goods sector have appeared in the rankings over the last two decades.

Places on graduate programmes at the leading consumer goods manufacturers are usually heavily oversubscribed, with more than 150 university-leavers competing for each vacancy in the sector in 2019.

"We call our programme the Unilever Future Leaders Programme, and I think that shows what we're trying to do in terms of creating leaders for the future for our business," says Selina Sykes, Category Development & Shopper Marketing Director at Unilever UK & Ireland.

"In the three-year programme, graduates get such an acceleration of personal development and such a range of opportunities, they are shaping the future of our business from day one," she explains.

The programme offers roles in marketing, sales (known as 'customer development' at Unilever), supply chain, finance, human resources, research & development and technology management, with a series of placements in different parts of the company.

"We look for people that can challenge the status quo, bring new ideas, dare to make the big decisions for our business, and people who want to make a difference," Sykes says. "I think for many graduates what's really exciting is the chance

Selina Sykes, Category Development & Shopper Marketing Director, Unilever

to work on some of the UK's most iconic brands. Our brands are in 98% of households in the UK and our goal is to use that connection to improve people's lives every day."

These brands are in three main categories – food & refreshment, home care and personal care – and include Ben & Jerry's, Lynx,

TOP 100
GRADUATE EMPLOYERS

CONSUMER GOODS
1. UNILEVER
2. P&G
3. L'ORÉAL
4. MARS
5. NESTLÉ
6. DIAGEO
7. MONDELĒZ INT'L (FORMERLY CADBURY'S, KRAFT)
8. DANONE
9. SONY
10. RED BULL

Source High Fliers Research
Top consumer goods employers of the last 20 years, based on their annual rankings in *The Times Top 100 Graduate Employers* 1999-2019.

Marmite, Cif, Hellmann's, Domestos, PG tips, Sure, Pot Noodle, Persil, Toni & Guy and Vaseline.

"For me personally when I joined as a graduate, once I understood the scope and breadth of Unilever as a global organisation, I was amazed to find a company that had so many brands that I loved in one place," recalls Sykes.

The first stages of Unilever's selection process for the Future Leaders Programme include an online application, tests and a digital interview.

The final assessment is what Unilever describes as a 'discovery centre day'. "We bring graduates in and ask them to solve real-world challenges using Unilever scenarios," says Sykes. "You're walking in, imagining that you're in a normal working day at Unilever and you're adapting and reacting and working in that way. It's good fun and an immersive experience for the people that come through the selection process. It's a great way to introduce Unilever, its work and its values."

Aim high
& Pioneer the
power that matters

Internship and graduate opportunities

Rolls-Royce pioneers cutting-edge technologies that deliver the cleanest, safest and most competitive solutions to meet our planet's vital power needs. Whether we're supporting NASA missions on the edge of space, collecting essential data about our planet or developing hybrid-electric propulsion systems for the next generation of flight, we're all about innovation.

Find out more about how you could help shape the world we live in. Visit **careers.rolls-royce.com**

Beyond tomorrow

Engineering & Industrial

From motor manufacturers and construction companies to steel producers, defence contractors and engineering design firms, twenty-four employers from the engineering & industrial sector have now appeared in *The Times Top 100 Graduate Employers*.

BAE Systems is one of just three major employers from the sector that have appeared in the rankings every year since 1999.

"We're delighted that so many of the country's top graduates continue to see us as an employer of choice," says Mark Rutherford, Director of Recruitment & Resourcing at BAE Systems. "The type of work we do – in the defence, aerospace and security sectors – is an opportunity for graduates to make a real difference. We're helping to protect those who protect us, and that appeals to many people's values and beliefs."

The company is planning to recruit around 300 graduates in the coming year. Around half of these vacancies will be in engineering, along with opportunities in procurement, HR and project management, as well as a five-year financial leadership development programme.

"We've recently changed the focus of our graduate programme, so that new graduates can accelerate their introduction into our business, make a greater impact straightaway in their role, and have the opportunity to progress at their own pace," explains Rutherford.

The programme begins with a three-week induction, to introduce graduates to BAE Systems, the sector and business unit they're joining, and the line manager they'll be working with for the next 18 months. "It's an exciting, immersive experience that includes seeing the company's products in action, whether that's at RAF Coningsby for our Typhoon

Mark Rutherford, Director of Recruitment and Resourcing, BAE Systems

jets or visiting a nuclear submarine," says Rutherford.

Showcasing the company's innovative technology is a key element of BAE Systems' recruitment strategy. "We know that graduate engineers can sometimes be tempted away into other career areas," Rutherford admits. "But for those who've been bitten by the bug of technology at university, they'll be excited by the potential products they could be working on here. To

have the chance to work on the next generation combat aircraft, the latest complex warship or cutting-edge cyber security is hugely appealing."

At the heart of BAE Systems' graduate programme is high-quality training. "We put a very strong focus on graduates' technical and personal development," says Rutherford. "We need individuals who are adaptable, collaborative and resilient. But it's not only about complex problem solving – we're also developing their creativity and emotional intelligence."

After successfully completing the programme, graduates can look forward to roles as technical specialists or functional leaders, depending on their interests.

"Because of the type of business that we are and the long-term nature of the work that we deliver, there's the opportunity for great career paths and an amazing number of different roles that you can move into, all within the same company," explains Rutherford.

"From a recruitment perspective, we're planning for the talent that we'll need for the next 20 years, and today's graduates are an essential part of that."

THE TIMES TOP 100 GRADUATE EMPLOYERS

ENGINEERING & INDUSTRIAL

1. **ROLLS-ROYCE**
2. **BAE SYSTEMS**
3. **ARUP** (FORMERLY OVE ARUP)
4. **ATKINS**
5. **JAGUAR LAND ROVER**
6. **AIRBUS**
7. **FORD**
8. **QINETIQ**
9. **SIEMENS**
10. **SCHLUMBERGER**

Source High Fliers Research
Top engineering & industrial employers of the last 20 years, based on rankings in *The Times Top 100 Graduate Employers* 1999-2019.

Picture this.

You're a brand-new Barclays graduate.

You believe we shouldn't ever settle for 'good'.

And so do the people around you.

You've got the space to run with your ideas.

To realise the downright extraordinary.

This is what it feels like to have

the backing of a world-class bank.

Because with us, there's more to discover.

There's more to become.

Graduate opportunities

joinus.barclays

BARCLAYS

Investment Banking

Helena Sharpe, Head of Campus Recruiting for EMEA, J.P. Morgan

The excitement of working in global finance and the promise of one of the world's most lucrative careers means that, over the last two decades, investment banking has remained a highly sought-after destination for ambitious new graduates.

A total of seventeen investment banks and asset management companies have now been ranked in *The Times Top 100 Graduate Employers*, with Goldman Sachs, J.P. Morgan and Citi appearing in every edition since 1999.

The graduate recruitment process for investment banking jobs starts almost at the very beginning of university. "We run 'spring week' programmes for first year students," explains Helena Sharpe, Head of Campus Recruiting for EMEA at J.P. Morgan. "You need to be organised and apply for them in the first few weeks of your degree, but they're a great introduction to the firm. And having one of these on your CV, either with us or another bank, definitely helps when you come to apply for a summer internship in your second year."

Like many of the top investment banks, J.P. Morgan recruits most of its graduates through these well-paid summer internships. "Internships are a competitive experience but we say to all of our interns that, if you perform, then we will give you a job," says Sharpe. "Naturally not everyone meets the bar, but the majority are offered a place on our graduate programme."

As well as being a fundamental part of banks' graduate recruitment processes, internships are also a reality check for applicants. "Students who want to go into banking often say they're prepared to work hard," Sharpe continues. "But that's what the internships are really about, to give people the chance to see first-hand what the environment and working life is like and decide whether it is for them."

J.P. Morgan's three biggest graduate programmes are markets (which includes sales, trading and research), investment banking and technology.

"Technology is actually the largest of these now," says Sharpe. "We've been running special showcase events in university computer science departments which include demonstrations of the different technologies that graduates could work on. It's been a good way to get the message across that there are interesting things happening in banks too, not just at the tech firms."

Sharpe is upbeat about J.P. Morgan's graduate recruitment in the year ahead. "We typically recruit around 500 graduates annually for our European operations, with 85% working in London," she explains. "We're expecting a very similar intake in 2020, although Brexit means there may be some changes of the location where graduates work. We're expanding in cities across Europe where we already have offices, including Frankfurt, Luxembourg and Paris."

"But we're still going to have a large presence in the UK," she reassures. "J.P. Morgan has always been forward-thinking in terms of its graduate hiring and, even after the crash in 2008, the firm continued recruiting graduates because they're its future."

THE TIMES

TOP 100
GRADUATE EMPLOYERS

INVESTMENT BANKING

1. **GOLDMAN SACHS**
2. **J.P. MORGAN**
3. **MORGAN STANLEY**
4. **CITI** (FORMERLY CITIBANK)
5. **UBS**
6. **DEUTSCHE BANK**
7. **BANK OF AMERICA MERRILL LYNCH**
8. **CREDIT SUISSE**
9. **STANDARD LIFE** (NOW ABERDEEN STANDARD)
10. **LEHMAN BROTHERS**

Source **High Fliers Research**
Top investment banks of the last 20 years, based on their annual rankings in *The Times Top 100 Graduate Employers* 1999-2019.

Law

There are more leading law firms featured in this edition of *The Times Top 100 Graduate Employers* than any other type of employer. With starting salaries averaging £45,000, the opportunity to train for a prestigious professional qualification, and the potential for a lifelong career, it's not hard to see why the top firms continue to be such a popular choice for new graduates.

Slaughter and May is one of the so-called 'Magic Circle' of elite international law firms and has been featured in the *Top 100* nineteen times in the last two decades.

David Johnson, one of the firm's Trainee Recruitment Partners, believes the firm offers a unique proposition for new graduates. "Our focus is on the more complicated bespoke-type transactional work, whether that be in the field of disputes, mergers & acquisitions or other areas, where we can bring to the table a more creative, thoughtful, cerebral approach," he explains.

"We are very different in our organisational structure too. We remain the only true partnership and, because we haven't opened our own offices internationally, we're smaller in terms of numbers of people, which breeds an air of collegiality. When an organisation grows above a certain size, I think that becomes very difficult to maintain."

Only around half of the graduates that Slaughter and May recruits are likely to have studied law for their undergraduate degree. "We believe great minds do think differently, and that's at the heart of what we look for," Johnson says. "We want graduates who are intellectually very curious and don't want to go into a job where they're not using that brain on a very regular basis."

David Johnson, Trainee Recruitment Partner, Slaughter and May

"Once non-law graduates have been through their conversion course and law school, and have spent two or three years with us, there is no difference in how they perform as lawyers," he continues. "For us, it's about recruiting the best people, and they won't all have studied law at university."

Up to 75 students take part in summer work experience at Slaughter and May each year, and a

LAW

1. **CLIFFORD CHANCE**
2. **ALLEN & OVERY**
3. **LINKLATERS**
4. **FRESHFIELDS BRUCKHAUS DERINGER**
5. **SLAUGHTER AND MAY**
6. **HERBERT SMITH FREEHILLS**
7. **EVERSHEDS** (NOW EVERSHEDS SUTHERLAND)
8. **DLA PIPER**
9. **HOGAN LOVELLS**
10. **BAKER MCKENZIE**

Source **High Fliers Research**
Top law employers of the last 20 years, based on their annual rankings in *The Times Top 100 Graduate Employers* 1999-2019.

number of these are offered training contracts with the firm. "We would love to be able to have more places on our summer schemes," says Johnson. "But we want to make sure our work experience involves students in the business, rather than sitting in a room being told what it's like. There's a big difference."

Slaughter and May typically recruits around 80 trainees each year, and isn't expecting this to change when the UK leaves the EU. "The firm is set up to take a long view on just about everything – the way we recruit and train people, the way we build client relationships, and the way we remunerate ourselves," reassures Johnson.

"We're not expecting Brexit to have an impact on our graduate recruitment – we're recruiting for the next 15 years, not the next three or four. Do we believe London will continue to be a primary centre for financial services? And will English law, with the exception of New York law, still be the most globally-used system of law? If the answer to those questions is yes, then there'll still be plenty for us to do and we will need bright young people to help us do it."

Public Sector

A record number of final year students from the 'Class of 2019' said that they wanted to 'give something back' to society when they started work after university, so it's no surprise that this year's applications to public sector employers far outstripped those for graduate jobs in law, accountancy and investment banking.

One employer that epitomises the spirit of public service after graduation is Teach First. Since its launch in 2002, it has recruited more than 14,000 of the UK's brightest graduates to teach in some of the country's most challenging schools.

Andrew Oliva-Hauxwell, Executive Director of Recruitment, Teach First

Teach First appeared as a new entry in *The Times Top 100 Graduate Employers* in 2003, reaching the top ten five years later, and it has been ranked a top five graduate employer for seven of the last eight years.

"We're very happy to have recruited our largest ever cohort of graduates in 2019," says Andrew Oliva-Hauxwell, Executive Director of Recruitment at Teach First. "A total of 1,735 graduates joined us this summer and, after five weeks' intensive training, started in schools in September, planning and teaching lessons."

This isn't just a record for Teach First, it's the largest number of graduates ever recruited by a single employer in the UK.

"The education system is hugely unfair because a parent's income is still such a big determinant of how well a child is likely to do at school," continues Oliva-Hauxwell. "We need graduates who care passionately about this and are prepared to spend at least two years teaching in a school in a low-income community in England or Wales. It could be anywhere from Blackpool to Hastings, as well as London, Manchester and Birmingham."

Teach First trains graduates to be both teachers and leaders. "We're recruiting the leaders of the future who can help end inequality in education, wherever they go on to work," he explains. "We work with corporate partners across a wide range of sectors who support us to achieve our vision. And many of these provide our trainees with opportunities to develop further skills through summer internships."

Over a thousand schools currently

THE TIMES

TOP 100

GRADUATE EMPLOYERS

PUBLIC SECTOR

1. **CIVIL SERVICE**
2. **NHS**
3. **TEACH FIRST**
4. **POLICE**
5. **LOCAL GOVERNMENT**
6. **MI5 - THE SECURITY SERVICE**
7. **MINISTRY OF DEFENCE**
8. **FRONTLINE**
9. **DSTL** (FORMERLY DERA)
10. **GCHQ**

Source High Fliers Research
Top public sector employer of the last 20 years, based on their annual rankings in *The Times Top 100 Graduate Employers 1999-2019*.

have at least one Teach First teacher, but there is demand for even more. "We've always had a real focus on quality because the graduates we put into schools need to be very bright, capable, ambitious and motivated," says Oliva-Hauxwell. "We want graduates who know their subject well, and 93% of our recruits this year have a 2.1 or a 1st".

Teach First trainees become qualified teachers during the programme and complete a Postgraduate Diploma in Education and Leadership (PGDE). "The deal is that it's a two-year programme, but a lot of people do fall in love with the profession and stay on, with 60% of past trainees currently in the classroom," he reflects. "We now have 60 headteachers that have been through the programme, and this number is always growing."

"Graduates who join Teach First will learn some amazing skills. They will learn about themselves and will have options open to them for the rest of their lives," he continues. "I don't think there are many professions where you can say on day one of your new role that you have made an impact on someone's life."

LIDL
YOU
LEAD
THE
WAY.
Choose our varied, comprehensive graduate programme to gain all-round experience and life-changing skills.
BRING YOUR BEST. WE'LL DO THE REST.
lidlgraduatecareers.co.uk

Retail

The retail sector in the UK has changed dramatically over the last two decades, with many of the country's best-known names struggling to reinvent themselves in the era of internet shopping and fast fashion.

A total of sixteen high street and online retailers have been ranked in *The Times Top 100 Graduate Employers* since its launch, with the long-established brands Marks & Spencer, Tesco and the John Lewis Partnership appearing in every edition since 1999.

But it is the discount supermarket which first appeared as a new entry at number 65 in 2002's *Top 100* that is now the runaway 'graduate employer of choice' for the retail sector. Aldi has been ranked among the country's top ten graduate employers for 13 years running and has spent the last five years in the top three.

"We are a responsible employer who thrives on giving graduates unparalleled levels of responsibility from day one," says Kelly Stokes, Recruitment Director at Aldi. "Our one-year area manager training programme prepares new graduates to take control of their own multi-million pound business at the end of their training, running up to four Aldi stores."

It is one of retail's most demanding entry-level training schemes. But in return, Aldi offers a market-leading starting salary of £44,000 along with a fully-expensed Audi A4 or BMW 3 Series company car.

"It's a highly structured training programme that introduces graduates to every aspect of our business and is an amazing foundation for their future success," explains Stokes. "Many of our high-performing area managers have gone on to become directors

Kelly Stokes, Recruitment Director, Aldi

and managing directors within the company, including our CEO, who started his career on the programme."

Aldi had over 40,000 applications for the hundred places available on its area manager programme in 2019, making it one of the most sought after destinations for new graduates.

THE TIMES TOP 100 GRADUATE EMPLOYERS

RETAIL

1. ALDI
2. MARKS & SPENCER
3. TESCO
4. JOHN LEWIS PARTNERSHIP
5. SAINSBURY'S
6. BOOTS
7. MCDONALD'S
8. LIDL
9. ASDA
10. ARCADIA GROUP

Source High Fliers Research
Top retail employers of the last 20 years, based on their annual rankings in *The Times Top 100 Graduate Employers* 1999-2019.

"We look for graduates who are incredibly hardworking and have the same positive can-do attitude that we have internally within the business," says Stokes. "Graduates need to be passionate about retail, driven, full of energy, full of enthusiasm, and confident communicators. And they need to be people-focused too because a big part of being an area manager is really driving and developing the store teams, so that they can deliver amazing customer service."

Aldi currently has more than 830 stores in the UK and expects to have at least 1,200 by 2025, by opening at least one new store a week over the next five years.

"Despite our size, there's still a real family-feel to working at Aldi. I'm really proud that the passion and enthusiasm our business has for its people matches how hard we work to get the prices and quality right for our customers," enthuses Stokes. "Everything we do is built on attitude. It's about never giving up and always striving for smarter, simpler ways of doing things."

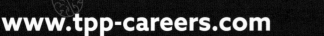

Technology

Amanda Timberg, Head of Talent and Outreach Programs in EMEA, Google

More than twenty employers from the fast-changing technology sector have featured in *The Times Top 100 Graduate Employers* over the last two decades, from IT firms and telecommunications providers to software developers and internet companies.

Google was listed among the UK's top graduate employers for the first time in 2005, rose up the rankings nine times in ten years, reaching the top ten for the first time in 2013, and has now appeared in the top five for five years running.

"I think graduates who are attracted to Google are attracted to our culture and to our scale," says Amanda Timberg, Head of Talent and Outreach Programs in EMEA. "Google is a company that thinks big, takes risks, and will always be that way – that's the fabric of the company. Graduates can see they would have the opportunity to come in, make an impact straight away and be innovating on helpful products that will be used all across the globe by billions of users."

Each year, Google runs an extensive programme of events and promotions to publicise its entry-level roles for graduates.

"For students interested in software engineering, one type of outreach we do is we take our engineers out to universities to talk about the new products they're working on and developing," explains Timberg. "And for those who are looking at sales, finance, legal and marketing roles, beyond going to conferences and universities to promote our roles, we also bring them onto our Google campuses to learn more about what we do, walk around the offices and experience the culture for themselves."

The company's distinctive culture is often cited as one of the main reasons for Google's success.

"It's definitely a fun place to work, and the look and feel of our offices is very different to more traditional companies," agrees Timberg. "For example, our founders wanted Googlers to have free food at work because they met at university and knew that, when people sit down together in a canteen, they're connecting with each other and thinking differently than they do in the office or a meeting room."

Google doesn't quote its graduate hiring numbers, nor does it necessarily recruit graduates to work in their home country. "We're a global company and are recruiting graduates from the UK, Europe and all over the globe, for jobs at many of our European offices, including Zurich, Munich, Dublin, London, Paris, Warsaw and Tel Aviv," says Timberg.

Unlike many other graduate employers, Google doesn't rely on a battery of online tests, games or automated video interviews to assess its applicants. "For technical positions there are coding exercises, but the main part of our selection process is always individual interviews," explains Timberg.

"There's not just one type of way to work at Google, so we're looking for people that bring new experiences and new perspectives. We're a place that really values passion, drive and curiosity, and if you have those attributes then Google will be a company that you'll really thrive in."

THE TIMES TOP 100 GRADUATE EMPLOYERS

TECHNOLOGY

1. **ACCENTURE** (FORMERLY ANDERSEN CONSULTING)
2. **IBM**
3. **MICROSOFT**
4. **BT**
5. **GOOGLE**
6. **VODAFONE**
7. **LOGICA**
8. **NORTEL NETWORKS**
9. **FACEBOOK**
10. **INTEL**

Source **High Fliers Research** Top technology employers of the last 20 years, based on their annual rankings in *The Times Top 100 Graduate Employers* 1999-2019.

Flight Lieutenant James "Hadders" Hadfield commands 'F' Flight on Tactical Communications Wing. He was sponsored by the RAF whilst studying his A-Levels and then at university where he read Electronic Engineering at the University of Birmingham.

James commands a Flight of 42 Cyberspace Communications Specialists whom are all experts on the systems that the RAF delivers. Be that Satellite Communications, Local Area Networks, Computer Systems, Applications and the defence of our networks from a diverse range of cyber threats.

"I could be deployed anywhere in the world as the lead communications specialist. I need to have an in depth understanding of the effect that the RAF is trying to achieve in order to deliver the communication systems that are required to support humanitarian aid and disaster relief; defence of the air; or the delivery of precision guided munitions from combat aircraft. Without communications you can't have air operations."

"The RAF is an organisation like no other because of our people and the world-class training that we receive. By investing in them, they always exceed our expectations, delivering in the most testing circumstances. No matter how big the challenge, the team always succeeds – that's why I love what I do."

ROYAL AIR FORCE
REGULAR & RESERVE

Flight Lieutenant Nosheen Chaudry is an Aerosystems Engineering Officer who has worked on several Squadrons including a GR4 Tornado Sqn at RAF Marham and on the Royal Air Force Aerobatic Team (RAFAT), The Red Arrows.

From early childhood Nosheen had a fascination with aircraft and the idea of flight. She was offered a RAF scholarship to be sponsored through Birmingham University to study engineering and now works around the cutting-edge aircraft used by the RAF.

"I fulfil a variety of roles, with responsibility for the teams maintaining aircraft within our fleet. It's challenging work but I like the fact I get posted from one station to another every two years to work on other related and sometimes different projects."

"One of the big attractions for me about the Royal Air Force is the sports and adventurous training on offer. I am really keen on athletics and have competed for the RAF Athletics Team for the last eight years." The RAF requires its personnel to keep physically fit and actively encourages adventurous training.

"I knew from an early age that this is the kind of thing I wanted to do and my family were very supportive in my career choice. In fact, they encouraged me to apply for the University Bursary which certainly helps with the cost of getting a degree."

For information about all of the roles available in the RAF, as well as sponsorship opportunities, visit the RAF Recruitment website. Search online for RAF Recruitment.

sTudent?

Stand out from the crowd with a subscription to The Times and The Sunday Times

As part of your subscription, you can enjoy:

Times+
Subscribers get access to events, discounts and deals, such as cinema tickets and more.

Reliable reporting
Where most papers rush, we collate and consider. Get more expert analysis and in-depth opinion.

Exclusive content
Access inspiring guides, videos and podcasts released throughout the year.

Save 92% on your subscription with full digital access for just 50p a week.

Purchase your subscription to start taking advantage of these benefits and many more. Visit thetimes.co.uk

Know your times

EMPLOYER	TOP 100 RANKING	ACCOUNTANCY	CONSULTING	ENGINEERING	FINANCE	GENERAL MANAGEMENT	HUMAN RESOURCES	INVESTMENT BANKING	LAW	LOGISTICS	MARKETING	MEDIA	PROPERTY	PURCHASING	RESEARCH & DEVELOPMENT	RETAILING	SALES	TECHNOLOGY	OTHER	NUMBER OF VACANCIES	PAGE
JAGUAR LAND ROVER	33			●					●					●			●			150-200	158
JOHNSON & JOHNSON	98			●	●						●			●		●				25-30	160
J.P. MORGAN	10	●			●	●	●	●										●		500+	162
KPMG	6	●	●		●	●	●											●		Around 1,200	164
L'ORÉAL	59				●						●					●				28	166
LIDL	24				●					●			●			●	●			60+	168
LINKLATERS	45								●											100	170
LLOYDS BANKING GROUP	23	●	●	●	●	●		●			●						●	●		200+	172
MARS	57			●	●	●	●				●		●	●		●				25-30	174
MCDONALD'S	88					●														30	176
MI5 - THE SECURITY SERVICE	55					●												●	●	200+	178
MORGAN STANLEY	41				●			●	●									●		200+	180
MOTT MACDONALD	97		●	●														●		280	182
NETWORK RAIL	72			●	●	●	●						●					●		250	184
NEWTON	19		●																	100	186
NGDP FOR LOCAL GOVERNMENT	64	●			●	●	●		●		●	●	●	●				●		140	188
NHS	5	●			●	●	●							●				●		500	190
NORTON ROSE FULBRIGHT	92								●											Up to 45	192
PENGUIN RANDOM HOUSE	44										●	●					●			200+	194
PINSENT MASONS	84								●											60-70	196
POLICE NOW	47																		●	350	198
PWC	2	●	●		●				●									●		1,350	200
RBS	25				●	●					●							●		250+	202
ROLLS-ROYCE	15			●																Up to 300	204
ROYAL AIR FORCE	71			●		●			●	●								●		500-600	206
ROYAL NAVY	53			●	●	●	●		●	●		●		●				●		No fixed quota	208
SANTANDER	65		●		●			●										●		50	210
SHELL	29			●	●	●	●				●			●		●	●			40+	212
SIEMENS	54			●	●	●							●	●		●	●			70-80	214
SKY	38		●		●						●							●		175	216
SLAUGHTER AND MAY	58								●											80	218
TEACH FIRST	8																		●	1,750	220
THINK AHEAD	36																		●	100	222
TPP	79									●				●		●	●			50+	224
UBS	60				●			●	●		●						●	●		100	226
UNILEVER	13			●	●	●				●	●			●		●	●			40-50	228
UNLOCKED	49																		●	130	230
VIRGIN MEDIA	75			●	●	●					●					●	●			60+	232
VODAFONE	87				●	●											●			149	234
WELLCOME	68			●	●	●	●					●		●			●			12	236
WHITE & CASE	93								●											50	238

GRADUATE VACANCIES IN 2019

Admiral

"Admiral is a fun place to work with plenty of opportunities to develop, learn new skills, and have a real impact on the company's success"

GRADUATE VACANCIES IN 2020
ENGINEERING
FINANCE
RESEARCH & DEVELOPMENT
TECHNOLOGY

NUMBER OF VACANCIES
50+ graduate jobs

LOCATIONS OF VACANCIES

In 25 years, the Admiral Group has evolved from a small start-up into one of the most profitable and innovative insurance companies in Europe. Data and technology take centre stage at this award-winning and multinational FTSE 100 company focused on FinTech.

As one of the top UK car insurance companies, Admiral relies heavily on data and technology to make effective decisions and maintain and improve their market position.

Functions such as pricing, data & analytics, and management information give graduates the opportunity to use cutting-edge techniques to contribute towards business success. Admiral Tech is another exciting business area, giving graduates exposure to the latest cloud technology, DevOps and agile environments. More recently, the Admiral Group has ventured into new areas, including Financial Services (AFSL) and Veygo. These entrepreneurial new businesses have a start-up mentality, with the benefit of being backed by a large and successful FTSE 100 company.

Admiral's data and technology roles are suited to graduates with a STEM degree, a numerical mindset and a willingness to learn and explore. Experience is not required, as graduates will benefit from full training and support to succeed and develop within their role.

Graduates at Admiral enjoy fantastic opportunities for career progression along with some unique benefits. Admiral believes in an informal, team-spirited environment where people pull together and have fun.

The company philosophy is that people who like what they do, do it better, and in 2019 Admiral was named *The Sunday Times*' best big company to work for in the UK!

STARTING SALARY FOR 2020
£21,000-£24,000
Plus £3,600 in shares every year
(after a year of service).

UNIVERSITY VISITS IN 2019-20
ABERYSTWYTH, BIRMINGHAM,
BRISTOL, CARDIFF, MANCHESTER,
SWANSEA, WARWICK
*Please check with your university careers
service for full details of local events.*

MINIMUM ENTRY REQUIREMENTS
2.1 Degree

APPLICATION DEADLINE
Year-round recruitment

FURTHER INFORMATION
www.Top100GraduateEmployers.com
*Register now for the latest news, campus
events, work experience and graduate
vacancies at Admiral.*

"Although it's an office job, it just doesn't feel like an office. Everyone is so friendly and relaxed. And I love putting my coding skills into practice"

Admiral

AECOM is a premier, fully integrated global infrastructure firm positioned to design, build, finance and operate infrastructure assets for governments, businesses and organisations. Formed in 1990, AECOM has over 87,000 employees worldwide and achieved over $20 billion in revenue for the fiscal year 2018.

AECOM graduates make a real difference to both the built and natural environment. The company is a leader in all of the key markets that it serves. AECOM services include building engineering, environment, bridges, roads, rail, water, surveying, project management, planning, power and architecture.

Delivering clean water and energy. Building iconic skyscrapers. Planning new cities. Restoring damaged environments. Connecting people and economies with roads, bridges, tunnels and transit systems. Designing parks where children play.

Worldwide, AECOM designs, builds, finances, operates, and manages projects and programmes that unlock opportunities, protect the environment, and improve people's lives.

The AECOM Graduate Development Programme lasts for two years, and will provide graduates with full financial and development support towards their relevant professional qualification, including mentoring, residential training modules, an opportunity to work on live client projects, external training courses where required, and multi-disciplinary exposure.

AECOM is seeking applicants from around 35 disciplines, including civil, structural, mechanical, electrical, building services, fire and sustainable buildings engineering, as well as quantity & building surveying, project management, planning & design, acoustics, water & power related disciplines, and environment including remediation, EIA, ecology, air quality, and GIS.

GRADUATE VACANCIES IN 2020

CONSULTING
ENGINEERING
FINANCE
PROPERTY

NUMBER OF VACANCIES
350 graduate jobs

LOCATIONS OF VACANCIES

STARTING SALARY FOR 2020
£24,000-£27,000

UNIVERSITY VISITS IN 2019-20
BATH, BELFAST, BIRMINGHAM, BRISTOL, CAMBRIDGE, CARDIFF, TRINITY COLLEGE DUBLIN, UNIVERSITY COLLEGE DUBLIN, DURHAM, EDINBURGH, EXETER, GLASGOW, HERIOT-WATT, IMPERIAL COLLEGE LONDON, LEEDS, LONDON SCHOOL OF ECONOMICS, LOUGHBOROUGH, MANCHESTER, NEWCASTLE, NOTTINGHAM, NOTTINGHAM TRENT, OXFORD BROOKES, PLYMOUTH, READING, SHEFFIELD, SOUTHAMPTON, STRATHCLYDE, SURREY, ULSTER, UNIVERSITY COLLEGE LONDON, WARWICK
Please check with your university careers service for full details of local events.

MINIMUM ENTRY REQUIREMENTS
2.2 Degree

APPLICATION DEADLINE
Year-round recruitment
Early application advised.

FURTHER INFORMATION
www.Top100GraduateEmployers.com
Register now for the latest news, campus events, work experience and graduate vacancies at AECOM.

AECOM

Connecting people and economies with roads, bridges, tunnels and transit systems. Delivering clean water and energy. Building iconic skyscrapers. Planning new cities. Restoring damaged environments. Designing parks where children play.

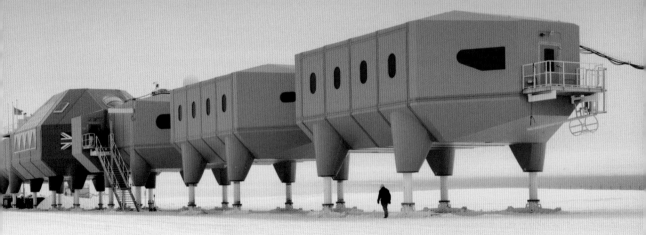

AIRBUS

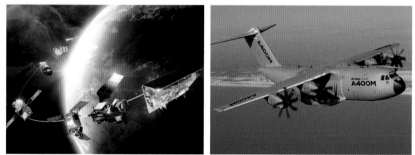

GRADUATE VACANCIES IN 2020

ENGINEERING
FINANCE
LOGISTICS
PURCHASING
RESEARCH & DEVELOPMENT
TECHNOLOGY

NUMBER OF VACANCIES
130+ graduate jobs

LOCATIONS OF VACANCIES

STARTING SALARY FOR 2020
£27,000
Plus a £2,000 welcome bonus.

UNIVERSITY VISITS IN 2019-20
ASTON, BRISTOL, CARDIFF, IMPERIAL
COLLEGE LONDON, LEEDS, LIVERPOOL,
LOUGHBOROUGH, MANCHESTER,
SHEFFIELD, SWANSEA
*Please check with your university careers
service for full details of local events.*

MINIMUM ENTRY REQUIREMENTS
2.2 Degree

APPLICATION DEADLINE
10th November 2019

FURTHER INFORMATION
www.Top100GraduateEmployers.com
*Register now for the latest news, campus
events, work experience and graduate
vacancies at Airbus.*

Airbus is an international pioneer in the aerospace industry and a leader in designing, manufacturing and delivering aerospace products, services and solutions to customers on a global scale. Its aim is for a better-connected, safer and more prosperous world.

Airbus graduates can take their first steps towards building a big career. Over the course of their programme, they can explore the breadth of the business through a series of three to six month rotational placements within disciplines such as engineering, finance, project management, business and IT – allowing them to build the knowledge, experience and understanding needed to progress within the organisation.

The Airbus UK graduate programme aims to accelerate learning development, helping graduates to discover new career paths and open their minds to the company's possibilities. It lasts between two to three years, and is both structured and flexible.

The placements are tailored to suit each graduate's needs, as well as those of the business, encouraging individuals to take control of their own career. Add to that outstanding training and development, a comprehensive induction, various technical and business modules, and graduates have everything they need to succeed in either their commercial aircraft or defence and space divisions. There is also the opportunity to take an optional Postgraduate Diploma in Engineering for further learning and development.

Airbus is a forward-thinking employer with a strong belief in a healthy work-life balance for its employees and supports flexible working. What's more, working alongside passionate and determined people, Airbus graduates will help to accomplish the extraordinary – on the ground, in the sky and in space.

Make it possible.
Make it happen.
Make it fly.

Prepare your Career
for Take Off!

Airbus designs, manufactures and delivers industry-leading commercial aircraft, helicopters, military transporters, satellites and launch vehicles, as well as providing data services, navigation, cyber and communications security, urban mobility and other solutions for customers on a global scale.

Our people work with passion and determination – we do what we love every day, working with talented individuals to make the best products even better. Our Internships and Graduate schemes give you the chance to work with us and make a difference – on the ground, in the air and in space.

See the full picture at
www.jobs.airbus.com

Follow us on:

in www.linkedin.com/company/airbusgroup

f www.facebook.com/airbuscareers

y @AirbusCareers

@WeAreAirbus

ALDI

GRADUATE VACANCIES IN 2020

GENERAL MANAGEMENT

RETAILING

NUMBER OF VACANCIES
100 graduate jobs

LOCATIONS OF VACANCIES

With roots dating back to 1913, Aldi (short for Albrecht Discount) came to the UK in 1990, and customers were amazed to see a fantastic example of 'no frills' shopping. Aldi are now one of the UK's fastest-growing supermarkets and one of the world's most successful retailers.

All graduates enter the business on the Area Manager Training Programme. It's gained a reputation for offering an enormous amount of responsibility, and rightly so. Over 12 months, graduates get everything they need to take control of a multi-million pound area of up to four stores. Graduates also receive incredible support throughout their training, with a dedicated mentor and regular one-to-one sessions with talented colleagues.

It's the perfect introduction to Aldi and a superb foundation for future success. It gives graduates a wider lens to make critical business decisions later on in their journey. Three to four years into the role, graduates may get the chance to take on a project role within one of Aldi's Regions, Corporate departments, Logistics, or even an International Secondment in countries such as the US or Australia. Further in the future, high-performing Area Managers could even move into a Director role within (for example) Corporate Buying, Finance or Operations.

Aldi is built on an attitude. It's about never giving up; always striving for smarter, simpler ways of doing things. They're a business with integrity: they're fair to their partners and suppliers, and everything they do is for the benefit of their customers and their people. They look for graduates who are incredibly hardworking with a positive, 'roll their sleeves up' attitude. Those who join Aldi will blend intellect with a practical, business-focused mindset as they achieve impressive results with a world-class team.

STARTING SALARY FOR 2020
£44,000

UNIVERSITY VISITS IN 2019-20
ASTON, BIRMINGHAM, BRISTOL, CARDIFF, EDINBURGH, EXETER, KEELE, LEEDS, LIVERPOOL, LOUGHBOROUGH, MANCHESTER, NEWCASTLE, NORTHUMBRIA, NOTTINGHAM, READING, ST ANDREWS, STRATHCLYDE, WARWICK, YORK
Please check with your university careers service for full details of local events.

MINIMUM ENTRY REQUIREMENTS
2.1 Degree
96 UCAS points
240 UCAS points for those who passed exams before 2017.

APPLICATION DEADLINE
Year-round recruitment
Early application advised.

FURTHER INFORMATION
www.Top100GraduateEmployers.com
Register now for the latest news, campus events, work experience and graduate vacancies at Aldi.

ALDI

It's been my biggest challenge.
And my greatest achievement.

Graduate Area Manager Programme
- **£44,000 starting salary (rising to £76,495 after four years)**
- **Pension • Healthcare • Audi A4/BMW 3 series**
- **All-year round recruitment but places fill quickly**

The Area Manager role gives graduates real responsibility and opportunities to progress. However, you'll need to have a 'roll your sleeves up' attitude, demonstrate your ability to lead a team and show a willingness to work outside your comfort zone. In return, we'll give you world-class training, a dedicated mentor, and support from your very first day. By the end of the year, you'll make a real contribution to the success of one of the UK's fastest-growing supermarkets. Amazing when you think about it.

aldirecruitment.co.uk/graduates

2018/19
The Guardian
UK 300

THE TIMES
GRADUATE RECRUITMENT
AWARDS 2019
'Graduate Employer of Choice'
RETAILING

ALLEN & OVERY

aograduate.com

twitter.com/AllenOveryGrads

facebook.com/AllenOveryGrads

instagram.com/AOmadeformore

linkedin.com/company/allen-&-overy

Allen & Overy is a leading global law firm operating in over 30 countries. It covers 99% of the world's economy, working with companies, organisations and governments on issues of incredible scope and complexity, applying new ways of thinking to the ever-changing world around us.

Allen & Overy are pioneers in the industry: the only firm to have topped the Financial Times Innovative Law Firm ranking six times. They look for trainees who want to push the limits of law, and in return who can expect a rewarding experience that will prepare them for a career at the very pinnacle of the profession. In each of their seats they'll support a senior associate or partner on work that crosses departments and borders – in fact, 74% of the firm's work involves two or more jurisdictions. Around 80% of trainees have the chance to spend six months in one of the firm's overseas offices, or go on secondment to one of its corporate clients.

As the world changes, the legal industry needs to evolve with it. A&O is investing in its people to ensure they have the skills and knowledge they will need to operate in the legal landscape of the future. For trainees, this means an in-house training programme characterised by flexibility, choice and opportunity – like having the chance to take a litigation course alongside their rotations.

A&O is dedicated to challenging the status quo and leading the way in commercial law. Around half have a degree in a subject other than law, so the firm is equipped to help its trainees develop into exceptional lawyers and learn to do work of the highest possible standard, regardless of their degree background. All they look for in return is for graduates to bring confidence, creativity and the desire to learn.

GRADUATE VACANCIES IN 2020
LAW

NUMBER OF VACANCIES
80-90 graduate jobs

LOCATIONS OF VACANCIES

STARTING SALARY FOR 2020
£Competitive
Plus a potential £10,000 maintenance grant for the A&O LPC, and also a £9,000 grant for the GDL in London.

UNIVERSITY VISITS IN 2019-20
BATH, BELFAST, BIRMINGHAM, BRISTOL, CAMBRIDGE, CARDIFF, TRINITY COLLEGE DUBLIN, UNIVERSITY COLLEGE DUBLIN, DURHAM, EDINBURGH, EXETER, IMPERIAL COLLEGE LONDON, KING'S COLLEGE LONDON, LEEDS, LEICESTER, LONDON SCHOOL OF ECONOMICS, MANCHESTER, NOTTINGHAM, OXFORD, QUEEN MARY UNIVERSITY LONDON, SHEFFIELD, ST ANDREWS, UNIVERSITY COLLEGE LONDON, WARWICK, YORK
Please check with your university careers service for full details of local events.

MINIMUM ENTRY REQUIREMENTS
2.1 Degree
136 UCAS points
340 UCAS points for those who passed exams before 2017.

APPLICATION DEADLINE
22nd December 2019

FURTHER INFORMATION
www.Top100GraduateEmployers.com
Register now for the latest news, campus events, work experience and graduate vacancies at Allen & Overy.

GRADUATE VACANCIES IN 2020
GENERAL MANAGEMENT
HUMAN RESOURCES
LOGISTICS
RETAILING
TECHNOLOGY

NUMBER OF VACANCIES
300+ graduate jobs

LOCATIONS OF VACANCIES

Vacancies also available in Europe, the USA, Asia and elsewhere in the world.

Amazon is driven by the excitement of building technologies, inventing products, and providing services that change lives. The company embraces new ways of doing things, makes decisions quickly, and is not afraid to fail. Come build the future with Amazon.

What unites Amazonians across teams and geographies is that they strive to delight customers and make lives easier. The scope and scale of the company's mission drives it to seek diverse perspectives, be resourceful, and navigate through ambiguity. Inventing and delivering things that were never thought possible isn't easy, but Amazon embraces this challenge every day. By working on behalf of its customers, Amazon is building the future one innovative product, service, and idea at a time. It's the job of Amazon employees to make bold bets. Success is measured against the possible, not the probable. For today's pioneers, that's exactly why there's no place on Earth they'd rather build than Amazon.

Amazon encourages graduates to have a self-starter mentality when it comes to learning and they supplement this with hands-on training to enable their people to progress and succeed.

There are opportunities across a broad spectrum of teams, and many of its graduates join the organisation as Area Managers, who - right from day one - are given significant responsibility to lead and develop teams of Amazon associates. The company hires the brightest minds and offers them the platform to be able to be able to think around corners and innovate on behalf of customers.

Amazon is an equal opportunities employer and believes passionately that employing a diverse workforce is central to its success. Recruiting decisions are based on having experience, skills and the passion to discover, invent, simplify and build.

STARTING SALARY FOR 2020
£Competitive
Plus a sign-on bonus and shares.

UNIVERSITY VISITS IN 2019-20
BATH, BIRMINGHAM, BRISTOL, CAMBRIDGE, TRINITY COLLEGE DUBLIN, UNIVERSITY COLLEGE DUBLIN, DURHAM, EXETER, GLASGOW, IMPERIAL COLLEGE LONDON, KING'S COLLEGE LONDON, LANCASTER, LIVERPOOL, MANCHESTER, NOTTINGHAM, OXFORD, UNIVERSITY COLLEGE LONDON, WARWICK
Please check with your university careers service for full details of local events.

APPLICATION DEADLINE
Year-round recruitment
Early application advised.

FURTHER INFORMATION
www.Top100GraduateEmployers.com
Register now for the latest news, campus events, work experience and graduate vacancies at Amazon.

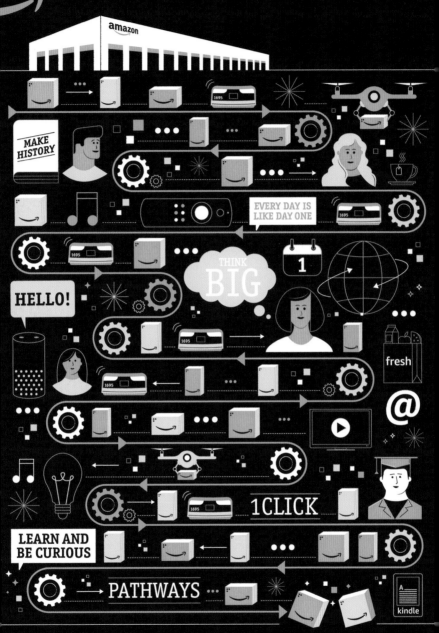

the impossible, possible.

blem solver? Curious to learn and innovate daily?
to learn to lead by example? If so, the Amazon Area
e in one of our many Fulfillment Centers could be the
for you. We will help you develop outstanding leadership
u will get to make history at one of the world's fastest
panies.

GRADUATE VACANCIES IN 2020

ACCOUNTANCY
ENGINEERING
FINANCE
GENERAL MANAGEMENT
HUMAN RESOURCES
LAW
LOGISTICS
MARKETING
MEDIA
PROPERTY
PURCHASING
RESEARCH & DEVELOPMENT
RETAILING
SALES
TECHNOLOGY

NUMBER OF VACANCIES
No fixed quota

LOCATIONS OF VACANCIES

STARTING SALARY FOR 2020
£Competitive

UNIVERSITY VISITS IN 2019-20
Please check with your university careers service for full details of local events.

APPLICATION DEADLINE
Year-round recruitment

FURTHER INFORMATION
www.Top100GraduateEmployers.com
Register now for the latest news, campus events, work experience and graduate vacancies at Apple.

Apple revolutionised personal technology with the introduction of the Macintosh in 1984. Today, Apple leads the world in innovation with iPhone, iPad, Mac, Apple Watch and Apple TV. Apple's software platforms provide seamless experiences across Apple devices and empower people with breakthrough services.

Apple does things differently, and the results have revolutionised entire industries. Every year, new graduates become a part of that as they start their career with Apple. This is a company that values curiosity and individuality, and provides opportunities to develop professional skills, get hands-on experience, and work with some of the best minds in the business.

Because Apple is at the intersection of technology and the liberal arts, the company hires great minds from every field of study. With so many ways to contribute, chances are good that employees will find a way to do what they love, whether they work in the UK or at one of Apple's locations around the world.

Apple seeks a wide variety of talent because it manages virtually every aspect of the business, from research and development, through manufacturing, to sales and support and even the customers' retail experience in the Apple Store. Beyond the roles that are focused directly on Apple technology, the company counts on talented people who can meet the challenges of running a unique global business. At Apple, this also means using its leadership position as a socially responsible corporate citizen to influence change in the world.

Everything Apple creates is the result of people working together to make each other's ideas stronger. That happens because everyone at Apple strives towards a common goal – creating the best customer experiences. And because Apple believes its most important resource is its people, it offers various benefits to help further the well-being of employees and their families in meaningful ways.

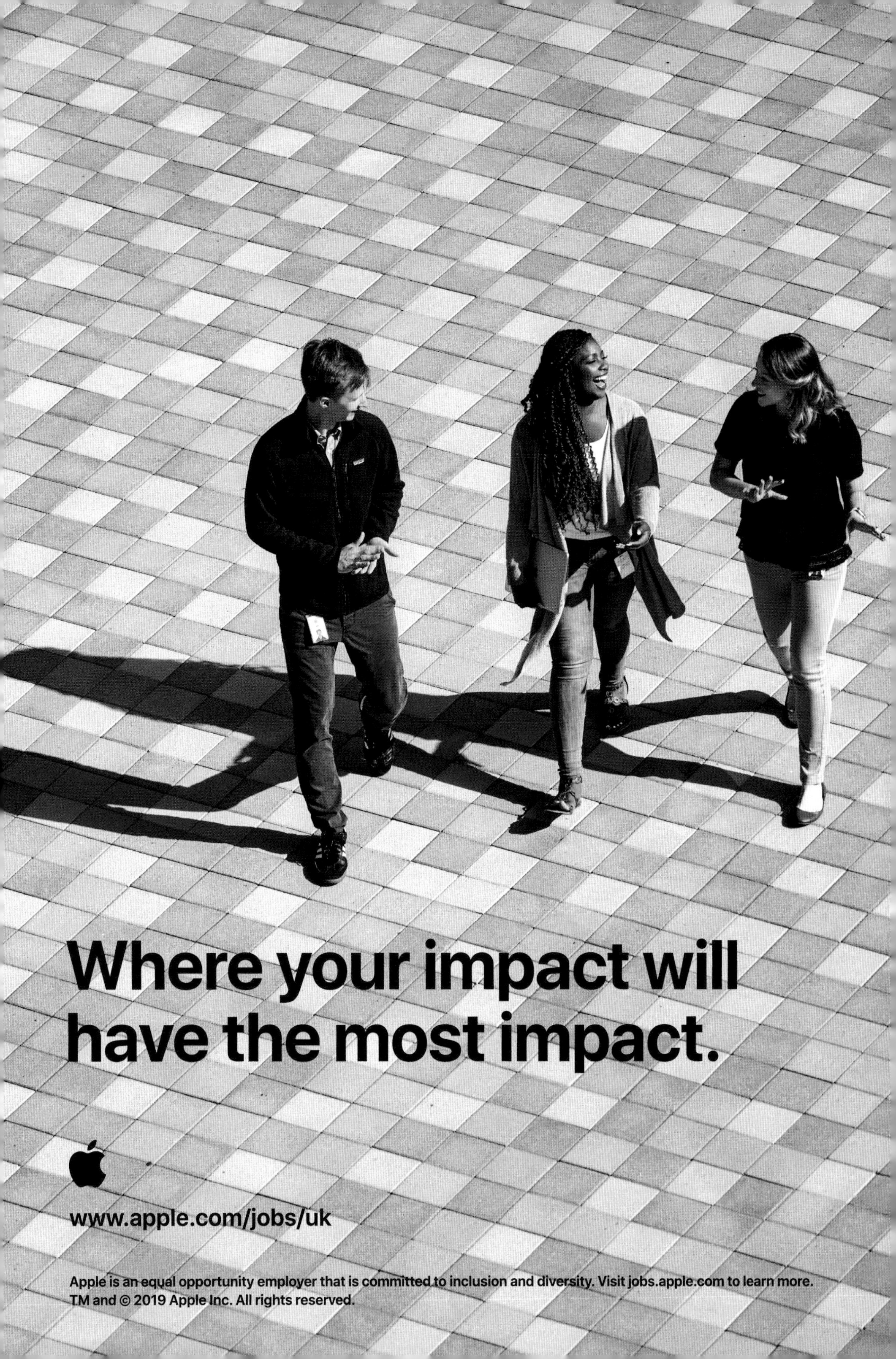

Where your impact will
have the most impact.
www.apple.com/jobs/uk
Apple is an equal opportunity employer that is committed to inclusion and diversity. Visit jobs.apple.com to learn more.
TM and © 2019 Apple Inc. All rights reserved.

ARMY
BE THE BEST

FIND WHERE YOU BELONG
SEARCH **ARMY OFFICER**

ARMY
BE THE BEST

Lead from the front, do something that really matters and serve the nation. Officers in the British Army have the responsibility of leading their soldiers to help make the world a safer, better place. The rewards are exceptional, the challenge is incredible and there's no bigger adventure in life.

The journey to becoming a British Army Officer begins at the Royal Military Academy Sandhurst, where Officer Cadets learn all the skills they need – from weapons handling to outdoor survival – and discover what it takes to lead their team and be responsible for the safety of the nation. Then, once they commission, they take command of a platoon of up to 30 soldiers and start the specialist training they need to be experts in their role – whether that's engineering, intelligence gathering or piloting an Apache helicopter.

From parachuting in the UK to sub-aqua diving overseas, Army Officers live an adventurous life, and take part in training around the world, all whilst earning a competitive salary. There are many benefits that come with Army life, from sports and state-of-the-art training facilities, to gaining professional qualifications and continually progressing their career. The Army also provides financial support for its future leaders, offering Army Undergraduate Bursaries to those who are interested in a career as an Army Officer after university, including a range of bursaries available for students of technical disciplines.

The Army looks for leadership potential, a sense of purpose and the drive to succeed. From the moment Officer Cadets join, they're set on a clear path for promotion and progression. With world-class leadership training and continuous support, Army Officers rise through the ranks to become influential leaders. Their life is full of challenge and adventure and it's a place where they can truly make a difference.

GRADUATE VACANCIES IN 2020
ENGINEERING
GENERAL MANAGEMENT
HUMAN RESOURCES
LAW
LOGISTICS
TECHNOLOGY

NUMBER OF VACANCIES
650+ graduate jobs

LOCATIONS OF VACANCIES

STARTING SALARY FOR 2020
Around £32,800
After training.

UNIVERSITY VISITS IN 2019-20
ASTON, BIRMINGHAM, CARDIFF,
DURHAM, EDINBURGH, ESSEX, EXETER,
GLASGOW, HERIOT-WATT, HULL, LEEDS,
LEICESTER, LIVERPOOL, LOUGHBOROUGH,
MANCHESTER, NORTHUMBRIA,
NOTTINGHAM, NOTTINGHAM TRENT,
OXFORD, PLYMOUTH, ST ANDREWS,
SWANSEA, ULSTER, WARWICK
*Please check with your university careers
service for full details of local events.*

MINIMUM ENTRY REQUIREMENTS
72 UCAS points
*180 UCAS points for those
who passed exams before 2017.*

APPLICATION DEADLINE
Year-round recruitment

FURTHER INFORMATION
www.Top100GraduateEmployers.com
*Register now for the latest news, campus
events, work experience and graduate
vacancies at the **British Army**.*

YOUR ARMY NEEDS YOU

YOUR ARMY NEEDS LEADERS.

The chance to do something that matters. Make your family proud as you make a difference to the world. Lead a team. As a British Army Officer, you'll live a life full of adventure and accomplishment. Your career has no limits, and with the opportunity to gain qualifications and adaptable skills, you'll become an incredible leader. You'll be awarded a starting salary of around £27,200, which will rise to around £32,800 upon completion of one year's training – and as you advance through the ranks, so will your salary.

Travel the world and lead your soldiers as you play a vital part in creating a sense of belonging that empowers all. We realise your potential and will support you to reach it.

Your Army needs leaders. Your Army needs you.

SEARCH
ARMY OFFICER

ARMY
BE THE BEST

asos

Authentic, brave and creative to their core. ASOS focus on fashion as a force for good, inspiring young people to express their best selves and find the confidence to achieve amazing things. They believe fashion thrives on individuality and should be fun for everyone.

ASOS is a global fashion destination for 20-somethings, selling cutting-edge clothes and offering a wide variety of fashion-related content that makes ASOS.com the hub of a thriving community.

ASOS sells over 85,000 branded and ASOS Brand products through localised app and mobile/desktop web experiences, delivering from their fulfilment centres in the UK, US and Europe to almost every country in the world.

Its curated mix of in-house designed labels and global and local brands delivers a locally relevant offer, available in eight languages in over 200 markets.

ASOS are thrilled to have been selected as a company where graduates aspire to work. They drive innovation through technology and continue to push the boundaries of online retail. In addition to a competitive salary, a 40% discount and a benefits package, every graduate is offered support and guidance throughout their time at ASOS.

ASOS are passionate about their people and want to help them develop professionally throughout their career by offering a range of bespoke and tailored learning solutions. Career coaching, mentors from within the business, team development days, career planning and sponsored qualification support are all part of what ASOS offers.

ASOS is the place to be for any graduates who like the idea of working in a fast-paced, innovative and supportive environment where everyone can be themselves and is passionate about what they do.

facebook.com/AstraZenecaCareers **f**

linkedin.com/company/astrazeneca **in** twitter.com/AstraZenecaJobs **y**

instagram.com/AstraZeneca_careers **O** youtube.com/AstraZeneca **▶**

GRADUATE VACANCIES IN 2020

ENGINEERING

GENERAL MANAGEMENT

LOGISTICS

RESEARCH & DEVELOPMENT

TECHNOLOGY

NUMBER OF VACANCIES
70+ graduate jobs

LOCATIONS OF VACANCIES

*Vacancies also available in Europe,
the USA, Asia and elsewhere in the world.*

STARTING SALARY FOR 2020
£30,000
*Plus a sign-on or relocation bonus
where appropriate.*

UNIVERSITY VISITS IN 2019-20
BIRMINGHAM, CAMBRIDGE, EDINBURGH,
IMPERIAL COLLEGE LONDON, KING'S
COLLEGE LONDON, LANCASTER, LEEDS,
LIVERPOOL, MANCHESTER, NOTTINGHAM,
OXFORD, SHEFFIELD, UNIVERSITY COLLEGE
LONDON, WARWICK, YORK
*Please check with your university careers
service for full details of local events.*

MINIMUM ENTRY REQUIREMENTS
2.1 Degree

APPLICATION DEADLINE
Varies by function

FURTHER INFORMATION
www.Top100GraduateEmployers.com
*Register now for the latest news, campus
events, work experience and graduate
vacancies at AstraZeneca.*

AstraZeneca is a global biopharmaceutical company, pushing the boundaries of science to deliver life-changing medicines that patients need and society values. AstraZeneca is now entering a new stage in their strategic journey, focused on enhanced innovation and sustainable growth.

Graduates from any discipline who are inspired by what science can do thrive in AstraZeneca's international and diverse culture. They have a unique spirit of collaboration and provide their graduates with real responsibility from day one, as well as the opportunity to contribute to ground-breaking projects and gain extensive understanding of the global biopharmaceutical industry, from discovery to patients.

Whatever path graduates follow to achieve their career objectives, they will benefit from a tailored personal development plan created in collaboration with experienced leaders. Mentors and graduate assigned 'buddies' will help set them up for success within an energising and entrepreneurial environment.

Some programmes offer graduates international opportunities to explore their potential as they progress. At every global location, graduates will find AstraZeneca offers a rich array of experiences, perspectives and challenges within a supportive environment that will help them achieve their potential.

AstraZeneca graduates work with bold thinkers whose ideas are as diverse as the culture that helped shape them. AstraZeneca is proud of their award-winning, progressive working practices, and recognises that diverse teams are innovative teams which strengthen connections between employees and patients, stakeholders and communities.

To find out more about the graduate opportunities available and how to discover what science can do, visit their careers site.

Join an AstraZeneca Graduate Programme and help push the boundaries of science to deliver life-changing medicines

We have exciting opportunities in the following areas:

- Operations
- IT
- Research and Development
- Data Science & AI
- Pharmaceutical Technology and Development

Starting salary for 2020

£30,000+

Plus bonus, benefits & relocation (if applicable)

AstraZeneca

ATKINS

Member of the SNC-Lavalin Group

Atkins, a member of the SNC-Lavalin Group, is a leading global consultancy, with over 80 years' design and engineering expertise. Driven to discovering new ways to answer the world's biggest challenges, they help clients to bring their projects to life and make a real difference to people's lives globally.

Atkins is searching for curious minds who ask questions and dare to do things differently. Graduates have the opportunity to be part of a wide variety of projects that can leave a lasting legacy, from helping to provide drinkable water in third world countries to solving the energy problems of the future. As a leading international consultancy, Atkins offers graduates the chance to work with major global clients from BAE Systems to High Speed 2. Graduates will find opportunities across a variety of areas from aerospace to energy, transport to technology.

With the Atkins three-year Graduate Development Programme, graduates can be sure that they are in great company. Supported by line managers, senior leaders, the Learning & Development team and the graduate community, they're given the trust and flexibility to drive their own development. They are part of a diverse environment where wellbeing and work-life balance is highly valued.

Atkins offers a graduate experience like no other, where graduates are surrounded by a wealth of design and engineering expertise. They gain the skills and knowledge to develop thriving early careers, supplemented by world-class training, including professional schemes that can lead to Chartered status. They benefit from a competitive package with a £2,500 settling-in bonus and a £2,500 bonus on achieving Chartership or professional registration, in addition to flexible holidays and volunteer days. Atkins invites graduates to join the minds who want to build a better world.

GRADUATE VACANCIES IN 2020
CONSULTING
ENGINEERING
TECHNOLOGY

NUMBER OF VACANCIES
400 graduate jobs

LOCATIONS OF VACANCIES

STARTING SALARY FOR 2020
£27,000-£30,500
Plus a £2,500 settling-in bonus, and a £2,500 bonus on achieving Chartership or professional registration.

UNIVERSITY VISITS IN 2019-20
BATH, BIRMINGHAM, BRISTOL, CARDIFF, DURHAM, EXETER, HERIOT-WATT, IMPERIAL COLLEGE LONDON, LEEDS, LOUGHBOROUGH, MANCHESTER, NEWCASTLE, NOTTINGHAM, NOTTINGHAM TRENT, OXFORD BROOKES, PLYMOUTH, READING, SHEFFIELD, SOUTHAMPTON, STRATHCLYDE, SURREY, SWANSEA
Please check with your university careers service for full details of local events.

MINIMUM ENTRY REQUIREMENTS
2.1 Degree

APPLICATION DEADLINE
Varies by function

FURTHER INFORMATION
www.Top100GraduateEmployers.com
Register now for the latest news, campus events, work experience and graduate vacancies at **Atkins**.

BAE SYSTEMS

baesystems.com/graduates
twitter.com/BAESgraduates   facebook.com/BAESgraduates

BAE Systems help their customers to stay a step ahead when protecting people and national security, critical infrastructure and vital information. This is a long-term commitment involving significant investments in skills. They also work closely with local partners to support economic development through the transfer of knowledge, skills and technology.

By demonstrating passion and enthusiasm to improve, graduates will receive the support needed to be creative and pioneering throughout their development, to set the stage for an amazing future with BAE Systems.

The BAE Systems graduate programme combines formal learning with valuable real-world experience, giving graduates the opportunity to develop in their chosen field from day one. BAE Systems place great importance not only on what they do, but how and why they do it. Their graduates are supported throughout the programme with training and mentoring, enabling them to make the very most of their talents and develop a career where they'll make a real difference.

For those with an interest in finance, there's the five-year Finance Leader Development Programme (FLDP) which is a fast-track finance graduate scheme, preparing individuals to become finance leaders of the future. The programme includes a structured and fully supported route to the highly respected Chartered Institute of Management Accountants (CIMA) qualification.

Alongside this, BAE Systems Applied Intelligence offer a range of early career positions in Consulting, Engineering and Project Management. Graduates will be involved in supporting the delivery of solutions which help clients to protect against cyber threats and enhance their critical assets in the connected world.

BAE Systems also have a number of summer internship and industrial placements available in a range of business, consulting, finance and engineering roles.

GRADUATE VACANCIES IN 2020
CONSULTING
ENGINEERING
FINANCE
GENERAL MANAGEMENT
HUMAN RESOURCES
TECHNOLOGY

NUMBER OF VACANCIES
Around 300 graduate jobs

LOCATIONS OF VACANCIES

STARTING SALARY FOR 2020
£28,000-£30,000

UNIVERSITY VISITS IN 2019-20
ASTON, BIRMINGHAM, BRISTOL, GLASGOW, KENT, LANCASTER, LIVERPOOL, LOUGHBOROUGH, MANCHESTER, NEWCASTLE, SHEFFIELD, SOUTHAMPTON, STRATHCLYDE, SURREY, UNIVERSITY COLLEGE LONDON, WARWICK
Please check with your university careers service for full details of local events.

MINIMUM ENTRY REQUIREMENTS
Requirements vary by function – please see website for details.

APPLICATION DEADLINE
Varies by functions
With multiple intakes throughout the year.

FURTHER INFORMATION
www.Top100GraduateEmployers.com
Register now for the latest news, campus events, work experience and graduate vacancies at BAE Systems.

Baker McKenzie.

Baker McKenzie prides itself on being the global law firm that offers a personal and professional approach to its graduates and clients alike. It's this approach that ensures the firm is ideally placed to offer graduates the best possible start to their legal career.

With 77 offices in 47 countries, and a presence in all leading financial centres, Baker McKenzie is the world's premier global law firm. London is home to the firm's largest office, where Baker McKenzie has been well established since its opening in 1961. With more than 400 lawyers, they deliver high-quality local solutions across a broad range of practices and offer global advice in conjunction with their international offices. With a strong international client base, Baker McKenzie have considerable expertise in acting on, and coordinating, complex cross border transactions and disputes.

The firm offers 1st Year Insight Schemes and Vacation Schemes, and these provide the ideal opportunity to experience what it's like to work for a City-based, global law firm. Training is provided to familiarise individuals with some of their typical transactions and to help them develop key skills. Baker McKenzie place great emphasis on involving candidates in 'live' work with both Associates and Partners.

The two-year training contract comprises four six-month seats, which include a transactional and a contentious seat along with the possibility of a secondment abroad or with a client. The training contract commences with a highly interactive and practical induction which focuses on key skills including practical problem solving, presenting and the application of information technology. Formal and informal reviews are undertaken to support Trainees' ongoing development.

GRADUATE VACANCIES IN 2020
LAW

NUMBER OF VACANCIES
33 graduate jobs
For training contracts starting in 2022.

LOCATIONS OF VACANCIES

Vacancies also available in Europe, the USA, Asia and elsewhere in the world.

STARTING SALARY FOR 2020
£48,000

UNIVERSITY VISITS IN 2019-20
BIRMINGHAM, BRISTOL, CAMBRIDGE, DURHAM, EXETER, GLASGOW, KING'S COLLEGE LONDON, LEEDS, LEICESTER, LONDON SCHOOL OF ECONOMICS, MANCHESTER, NOTTINGHAM, OXFORD, QUEEN MARY LONDON, SHEFFIELD, UNIVERSITY COLLEGE LONDON, WARWICK, YORK
Please check with your university careers service for full details of local events.

MINIMUM ENTRY REQUIREMENTS
2.1 Degree
136 UCAS points
340 UCAS points for those who passed exams before 2017.

APPLICATION DEADLINE
Varies by function

FURTHER INFORMATION
www.Top100GraduateEmployers.com
*Register now for the latest news, campus events, work experience and graduate vacancies at **Baker McKenzie**.*

The impact of the Bank of England's work is uniquely far-reaching. As the country's central bank, they promote the good of the people of the UK by maintaining monetary and financial stability. The work they do, and the decisions they make, influences the daily lives of millions of people.

The Bank's primary role hasn't changed for over 300 years. But the range of work they do, and the ways in which they deliver it, is changing all the time. Today it's changing quicker than ever before. And their graduates are a key part of this progress.

Despite the nature of the Bank's work, economics is not the only way in. They welcome graduates from all degree disciplines, because quality of thinking is what counts here. Their culture is open and collaborative, where ideas are shared freely and people at every level are empowered to speak up. It is refreshingly diverse too. The Bank looks for people from all backgrounds, and individual perspectives are embraced. Successful applicants will find a wide range of societies, clubs and employee networks open to them.

Wherever graduates work – from Regulation, Technology and Policy Analysis to Economics and Communications – they'll take on complex work that they can be proud of. They'll tackle projects that support, shape and challenge the biggest ideas in the economy. And the work they do will benefit every single person in the UK.

As training is at the heart of the Bank's programme, graduates will be able to grow into real experts in their field. Equally, the support is there to explore other parts of the Bank if they wish. There are many and varied pathways available. Graduates who are keen to broaden their horizons will have every opportunity to define their own future as the Bank itself moves forward.

GRADUATE VACANCIES IN 2020

FINANCE
GENERAL MANAGEMENT
INVESTMENT BANKING
TECHNOLOGY

NUMBER OF VACANCIES
70+ graduate jobs

LOCATIONS OF VACANCIES

STARTING SALARY FOR 2020
£30,000

UNIVERSITY VISITS IN 2019-20
BRISTOL, DURHAM, EXETER, KING'S COLLEGE LONDON, LEEDS, LONDON SCHOOL OF ECONOMICS, MANCHESTER, QUEEN MARY LONDON, SHEFFIELD, SURREY, UNIVERSITY COLLEGE LONDON, WARWICK
Please check with your university careers service for full details of local events.

MINIMUM ENTRY REQUIREMENTS
2.1 Degree

APPLICATION DEADLINE
November 2019

FURTHER INFORMATION
www.Top100GraduateEmployers.com
Register now for the latest news, campus events, work experience and graduate vacancies at the Bank of England.

BANK OF ENGLAND

PICTURE WHAT TOMORROW'S ECONOMY COULD BE THEN GUIDE IT

We have one clear aim — to ensure stability at the heart of the UK's economy. But there are countless ways in which you could help us achieve this. From HR and Technology to Economics and Risk, you'll be encouraged and supported to follow the path that inspires you the most. And you'll enjoy real influence — not just over the projects you're involved in, but also over where your future with us goes next.

The Bank of England is changing today. **You define tomorrow.**

bankofenglandearlycareers.co.uk

Barclays is a transatlantic consumer, corporate and investment bank offering products and services across personal, corporate and investment banking, credit cards and wealth management, with a strong presence in its two home markets of the UK and the US.

Healthy economies need innovative banks to help transform and drive social progress. Barclays' ambition for bigger thinking is simple. By encouraging fresh ideas they can make a bigger difference. Interns and graduates at Barclays have many opportunities to get involved. To share big ideas. To show a better way. And to challenge what's already been done.

With over 325 years of history and expertise in banking, Barclays operates in over 40 countries and employs approximately 85,000 people. Barclays moves, lends, invests and protects money for customers and clients worldwide.

Barclays was the first bank to appoint a female bank manager, introduce ATMs, and launch credit cards and contactless payment. From the products and services they develop to the partnerships they build, they seek to improve lives and drive growth that benefits everyone.

Those joining can expect immediate responsibility. Collective challenges and inspiring collaborations will expand their minds, while ongoing training will turn fledgling ideas into groundbreaking concepts, providing the expertise that drives the bank and profession as a whole.

Barclays offers a wealth of opportunities for students from all degree disciplines. All graduates need is a commercial outlook, curious nature, and the ambition to help Barclays become the best bank it can be. In a positive, supportive environment, graduates will have the freedom to create smarter solutions every day.

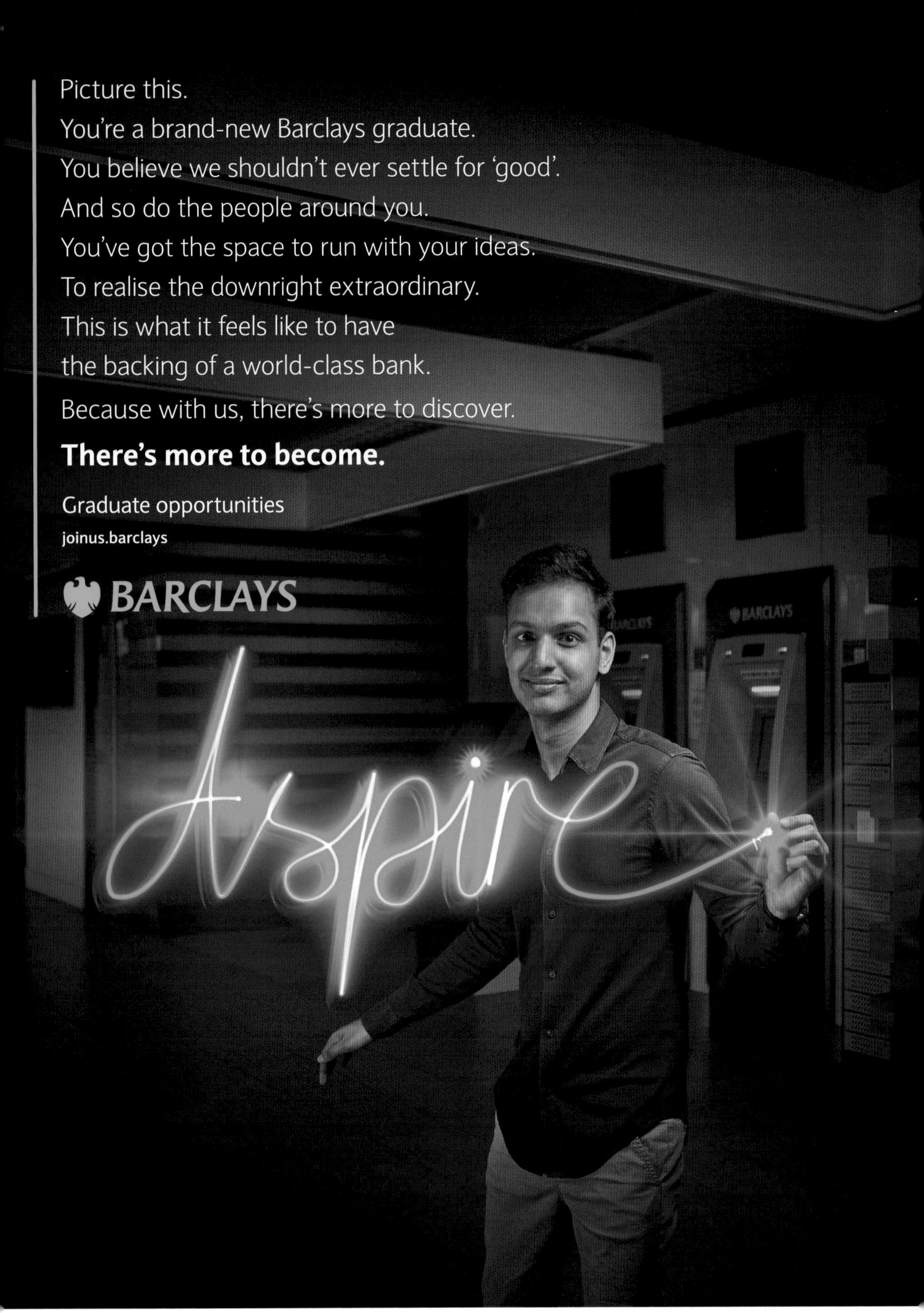

Picture this.

You're a brand-new Barclays graduate.

You believe we shouldn't ever settle for 'good'.

And so do the people around you.

You've got the space to run with your ideas.

To realise the downright extraordinary.

This is what it feels like to have

the backing of a world-class bank.

Because with us, there's more to discover.

There's more to become.

Graduate opportunities

joinus.barclays

BARCLAYS

BBC

The BBC is the world's leading public service broadcaster, creating distinctive, world-class programmes and content which inform, educate and entertain millions of people in the UK and around the world. More than 20,000 staff work at the BBC in corporate functions, journalism, production and technology.

The BBC provides a wide range of programmes, content and services for audiences across the UK on television, radio and digitally.

Opportunities for graduates are available across most of its functions, with its design and engineering division being a key area for growth in its 2019/20 recruitment season.

Structured entry-level trainee schemes for graduates are available in Broadcast Engineering, Software Engineering, Research and Development, UX Design, Communications, Journalism and Production. Graduates should expect a mix of placements and training periods, working on products and services that are enjoyed every day by millions of people.

Attitude, curiosity and passion are likely to impress BBC recruiters, as is a good dose of life experience and the ability to communication and work in a team and innovate. New perspectives are important to the BBC, and competition for places is tough. Being able to demonstrate motivation for the role through extra-curricular activities is really important.

Recruitment takes place at various times throughout the year; the BBC's careers website details the trainee programmes available for 2020 including expected open dates for applications. New opportunities do spring up throughout the year though, so interested students should register for email alerts on the BBC's careers hub to ensure they are kept up to date. Most trainee programmes start in September.

GRADUATE VACANCIES IN 2020

ENGINEERING
MEDIA
RESEARCH & DEVELOPMENT
TECHNOLOGY

NUMBER OF VACANCIES
50+ graduate jobs

LOCATIONS OF VACANCIES

STARTING SALARY FOR 2020
£21,216

UNIVERSITY VISITS IN 2019-20
Please check with your university careers service for full details of local events.

APPLICATION DEADLINE
Varies by function

FURTHER INFORMATION
www.Top100GraduateEmployers.com
Register now for the latest news, campus events, work experience and graduate vacancies at BBC.

Be part of something special. Join the BBC.

Opportunities in Broadcast Engineering, Software Engineering, Research & Development, User Experience, Journalism, Production and more.

To find out more, visit www.bbc.co.uk/careers

GRADUATE VACANCIES IN 2020
ACCOUNTANCY
FINANCE

NUMBER OF VACANCIES
380 graduate jobs

LOCATIONS OF VACANCIES

STARTING SALARY FOR 2020
£Competitive
Plus a range of benefits.

UNIVERSITY VISITS IN 2019-20
ASTON, BATH, BIRMINGHAM, BRISTOL, CAMBRIDGE, CARDIFF, CITY, DURHAM, EDINBURGH, ESSEX, EXETER, GLASGOW, HERIOT-WATT, HULL, IMPERIAL COLLEGE LONDON, KING'S COLLEGE LONDON, KENT, LANCASTER, LEEDS, LEICESTER, LIVERPOOL, LONDON SCHOOL OF ECONOMICS, MANCHESTER, NEWCASTLE, NOTTINGHAM, OXFORD, QUEEN MARY LONDON, READING, SOUTHAMPTON, STIRLING, STRATHCLYDE, SURREY, SUSSEX, UEA, UNIVERSITY COLLEGE LONDON
Please check with your university careers service for full details of local events.

MINIMUM ENTRY REQUIREMENTS
2.2 Degree

APPLICATION DEADLINE
Year-round recruitment
Early application is advised.

FURTHER INFORMATION
www.Top100GraduateEmployers.com
Register now for the latest news, campus events, work experience and graduate vacancies at BDO.

BDO is one of the UK's largest accountancy and business advisory firms. With more than 5,000 talented people, BDO provides integrated advice and solutions to help businesses succeed. Their clients are the ambitious, entrepreneurial and high-growth businesses that fuel Britain's economy.

BDO offers graduate programmes specialising in audit, tax, advisory and business services & outsourcing. Trainees are a fundamental and valued part of the organisation, central to the firm's plans for growth.

They're looking for people who are hungry to learn and who bring their personalities as well as their own unique skill set to the table. Those who take initiative, find imaginative solutions and question how things work are at the forefront of BDO's operations.

BDO provides graduates all the training they need to attain their professional qualifications, along with extensive practical experience that includes on-site client work. Ownership and responsibility are encouraged from the outset. This means that trainees can expect a range of tasks and challenges aligned to their position and their own unique goals. BDO provides coaching and support to give trainees a head start on their career journey into the world of business and accounting, as well as helping to build a professional network.

BDO's work is simple - helping businesses succeed - and they take the time to get to know their client's specific needs, business environment and industry. BDO clients enjoy working with people who can confidently advise them through new and unfamiliar territory, providing practical and insightful advice and solutions.

Life at BDO means being part of an agile and innovative organisation where trainees benefit from fast-tracked development and can shape their own career.

BEGIN YOUR DREAM JOB

Graduate programmes at BDO

We inspire our people to reach their full potential, offering talented graduates ongoing training and support on our Graduate programme. Ensuring you're set up for success, we'll help you to confidently advise our clients whilst working towards a respected professional qualification.

We accept any degree discipline with programmes across Audit, Tax, Advisory and Business Services & Outsourcing.

Get on the path
to a rewarding career
bdoearlyincareer.co.uk

BlackRock

GRADUATE VACANCIES IN 2020
CONSULTING
FINANCE
HUMAN RESOURCES
INVESTMENT BANKING
LAW
MARKETING
SALES
TECHNOLOGY

NUMBER OF VACANCIES
140 graduate jobs

LOCATIONS OF VACANCIES

Vacancies also available in Europe.

STARTING SALARY FOR 2020
£Competitive

UNIVERSITY VISITS IN 2019-20
Please check with your university careers service for full details of local events.

APPLICATION DEADLINE
Varies by function

FURTHER INFORMATION
www.Top100GraduateEmployers.com
*Register now for the latest news, campus events, work experience and graduate vacancies at **BlackRock**.*

What does BlackRock do? One answer is: BlackRock manages more assets than any other firm in the world. But what BlackRock does is far, far bigger than that. BlackRock helps more and more people experience financial well-being. That's what BlackRock does.

BlackRock brings together financial leadership, worldwide reach and state-of-the-art technology to provide answers to the millions of investors who entrust their financial futures to the company.

The story of BlackRock's success rests not just with its founders, but with the thousands of talented people who have brought their ideas and energy to the firm every day since. That's why BlackRock is looking for fresh perspectives and new ideas, and views its differences as strengths. It knows that its success depends on its ability to use collective experiences and ideas to achieve more for its clients and the business.

BlackRock strongly believes that diverse skill-sets and perspectives lead to more innovative solutions and better results. Being part of BlackRock means joining a community of talented, smart, ambitious people. People who value diversity of thought and background, who believe everyone has a voice at the table. BlackRock's student programmes are an ideal opportunity for problem solvers, innovators and future leaders to work at a firm that has been called on by some of the world's largest companies and governments to find solutions for their most pressing financial challenges.

At BlackRock, students can have a career that's exciting, rewarding and full of possibilities and opportunities. BlackRock offers roles in advisory & client services; analytics & risk; corporate functions & operations; investments; relationship management & sales; and technology.

Discover a different path

BlackRock is a global investment firm, trusted to manage more assets than any other. We're responsible for the financial wellbeing of governments, foundations, and people saving for retirement, their children's education and hopes of a better life. Which gets to our purpose. We help more and more people experience financial wellbeing.

BlackRock employees from around the globe are students of the market and students of technology, respectfully anti-bureaucratic, and innovative at the core. If that sounds like you, discover a different path at: **careers.blackrock.com/campusrecruitment**

BlackRock.

Bloomberg

bloomberg.com/careers

twitter.com/BloombergCareer 🐦 facebook.com/BloombergCareers f
instagram.com/Bloomberg 📷 linkedin.com/company/bloomberg-lp in

As a global information and technology company, Bloomberg use its dynamic network of data, ideas and analysis to solve difficult problems every day. Its customers around the world rely on them to deliver accurate, real-time business and market information that helps them make important financial decision.

Bloomberg is guided by four core values: innovation, collaboration, customer service, and doing the right thing. The new European Headquarters in London is a testament to that innovation, as it's the world's most sustainable office building.

Bloomberg offers internships and full-time entry-level roles at their London office across a range of business areas including Analytics & Sales, Engineering, Global Data, Operations, and more. Candidates who join Bloomberg can build and define their own unique career, rather than a pre-defined path. Bloomberg is proud to have a truly global dynamic organisation, so all employees are empowered to have an impact and are measured by their contributions. All graduate starters will participate in team-specific training that continues throughout their career via robust career development resources.

Bloomberg also offers internships to provide an unparalleled combination of learning, networking, and project responsibilities. The internship programme aims to provide first-hand exposure to its business and unique culture, and is filled with training, seminars, senior leader speaker series, philanthropic events, and more.

Candidates apply online on Bloomberg's career website. The interview process will depend on the business area they have applied to, but typically involves a video and/or telephone interview followed by in-person interviews and assessment days. Bloomberg hire on a rolling basis, so early application is advised.

GRADUATE VACANCIES IN 2020
ENGINEERING
FINANCE
MEDIA
SALES

NUMBER OF VACANCIES
529 graduate jobs

LOCATIONS OF VACANCIES

STARTING SALARY FOR 2020
£Competitive
Plus a competitive bonus.

UNIVERSITY VISITS IN 2019-20
BATH, BRISTOL, CAMBRIDGE, TRINITY COLLEGE DUBLIN, EDINBURGH, GLASGOW, IMPERIAL COLLEGE LONDON, KING'S COLLEGE LONDON, LONDON SCHOOL OF ECONOMICS, MANCHESTER, OXFORD, QUEEN MARY LONDON, SOUTHAMPTON, ST ANDREWS, UNIVERSITY COLLEGE LONDON, WARWICK
Please check with your university careers service for full details of local events.

APPLICATION DEADLINE
Year-round recruitment
Early application advised.

FURTHER INFORMATION
www.Top100GraduateEmployers.com
*Register now for the latest news, campus events, work experience and graduate vacancies at **Bloomberg**.*

How does
a tsunami
affect
microchip
prices?

At Bloomberg,
we ask hard questions
and then build tools
to answer them.
It's our purpose.

Come find yours.
bloomberg.com/careers

Make connections **on purpose.**

Sarah / Marketing

Bloomberg

© Bloomberg L.P. 219543 2018

GRADUATE VACANCIES IN 2020

FINANCE
GENERAL MANAGEMENT
HUMAN RESOURCES
MARKETING
TECHNOLOGY

NUMBER OF VACANCIES
30-40 graduate jobs

LOCATIONS OF VACANCIES

Boots is the UK's leading pharmacy-led health and beauty retailer, and has been blazing a trail over the last 170 years. It's an exciting time to be part of this global enterprise, which is undergoing real transformation: from creating a market-leading omni-channel pharmacy experience to reinventing beauty.

As a member of Walgreens Boots Alliance, Boots continues to leverage its global experience and expertise to care for people and the planet through numerous social responsibility and sustainability initiatives that have an impact on the health and well-being of people both here in the UK and internationally.

Now is the time to be part of this exciting transformation and make a mark. Boots offers a wide variety of undergraduate and graduate programmes to kick start careers from Pre-reg Pharmacist and Optician opportunities across the UK to Support Office opportunities based in Nottingham.

Each programme offers a unique blend of learning, combining face-to-face and digital modules with practical on-the-job experiences to support personal and professional development. The programmes help to develop skills and knowledge, and provide all the stretch and challenge needed to accelerate a career at Boots.

There is an opportunity to gain a true breadth and depth of experiences and to take real accountability from day one, with ambitious goals and high challenge, and in return graduates will receive all the care, encouragement and support they need.

Boots are looking for individuals who thrive in a fast-paced environment; who are agile, innovative, and passionate with real leadership potential; who are not fazed by any challenges that come their way; and who want to make a real difference, to contribute and to shape the future at Boots.

STARTING SALARY FOR 2020
£26,000
£29,000 for Software Engineering.

UNIVERSITY VISITS IN 2019-20
LEICESTER, LOUGHBOROUGH,
NOTTINGHAM, NOTTINGHAM TRENT,
SHEFFIELD
*Please check with your university careers
service for full details of local events.*

MINIMUM ENTRY REQUIREMENTS
2.1 Degree

APPLICATION DEADLINE
Varies by function

FURTHER INFORMATION
www.Top100GraduateEmployers.com
*Register now for the latest news, campus
events, work experience and graduate
vacancies at **Boots**.*

the bigger picture

whichever way you look at it
#boots360

bp

BP delivers energy products and services around the world. From finding, developing and producing oil and gas resources, to refining, manufacturing and selling related products directly to customers and on the global markets, it keeps the world moving.

Today's growing world demands more energy – but in new ways with fewer emissions. BP is a global energy business, working towards producing cleaner energy, while lowering carbon in a safe, sustainable and consistent way – to help the world keep advancing.

It is only by bringing together diverse people in one, world-class team that everyone succeeds. BP's engineers, technology developers, geoscientists, traders, HR professionals, commercial analysts and many more all have a huge part to play in solving challenges like this. When joining one of their Early Talent Programmes, young professionals have a part to play too.

BP's internship and graduate programmes give new joiners a platform to become business leaders, leading scientists or ground-breaking engineers; offering plenty of opportunities to make a real contribution, while helping them to achieve their full potential. Their paid 11-week and year-long internships offer hands-on business experience to undergraduates or postgraduates who are about to start the final year of their degree or PhD. Graduates on their two- or three-year programmes have a chance to gain a full range of skills and experience too.

BP's diverse and inclusive environment focuses on teamwork, respect and ambition, as much as on academic achievements. From day one, students are offered a real chance to build a challenging, varied career and to contribute at any stage of the energy life cycle. At BP, everyone can achieve their goals, while making a meaningful impact for millions.

GRADUATE VACANCIES IN 2020

ACCOUNTANCY
ENGINEERING
FINANCE
HUMAN RESOURCES
LOGISTICS
PURCHASING
RESEARCH & DEVELOPMENT
RETAILING
SALES
TECHNOLOGY

NUMBER OF VACANCIES
100+ graduate jobs

LOCATIONS OF VACANCIES

STARTING SALARY FOR 2020
£35,000+
Plus a £3,000 settling-in allowance.

UNIVERSITY VISITS IN 2019-20
ABERDEEN, BATH, BIRMINGHAM, CAMBRIDGE, DURHAM, LEEDS, IMPERIAL COLLEGE LONDON, LONDON SCHOOL OF ECONOMICS, LOUGHBOROUGH, MANCHESTER, NOTTINGHAM, OXFORD, SHEFFIELD, STRATHCLYDE, UNIVERSITY COLLEGE LONDON
Please check with your university careers service for full details of local events.

MINIMUM ENTRY REQUIREMENTS
2.1 Degree

APPLICATION DEADLINE
Varies by function

FURTHER INFORMATION
www.Top100GraduateEmployers.com
Register now for the latest news, campus events, work experience and graduate vacancies at BP.

Our vision
of the future
is changing.

Ready to be part
of a brighter world?

Today's growing world demands more energy – but in new ways with fewer emissions. It is only by bringing together diverse people in one, world-class team, that we will succeed. BP's engineers, technology developers, geoscientists, traders, HR professionals, commercial analysts and many more, all have a huge part to play in solving challenges like this. For an internship or graduate programme that could help the world keep advancing, apply at **bp.com/grads/uk**

keep advancing

BE PART OF
PROGRESS

Every day, BT's people are able to touch the lives of millions, providing the key services everyone needs to get the most out of life. BT knows that with great power, comes great responsibility. That's why they are committed to a much higher purpose – to use the power of communication to create a better world.

The company's reach spans far and wide across the globe, operating in over 180 countries – making them one of the world's leading and most diverse communication providers. It's little wonder then that BT is one of the top picks when it comes to their graduate opportunities and schemes.

As graduates know all too well, the world today brings many challenges for those starting out in the ever-changing and highly competitive world of work. In response to this, BT is on a mission to help eager grads to kick-start their careers, encouraging them to adapt and reinvent themselves, as their roles, values and skillsets shift and grow around them. In this respect, the company is offering the young talent of today something completely unique – the promise of a diverse career in a company that doesn't stand still.

Diversity is at the very heart of BT. In order to provide the very best products and services to a varied customer base, they need a diverse workforce to imagine, create and deliver solutions, required both now and in the future. This means creating and maintaining a working environment that includes and values graduates.

BT's commitment to creating a diverse and people-led business is the driving force behind their core purpose. So any graduate who is ready to embrace the dynamic world of work, and who is seeking an environment that provides them with the space to discover their strengths, will be right at home. This could be the perfect time to join their cause and Be Part of Progress.

GRADUATE VACANCIES IN 2020

GENERAL MANAGEMENT
HUMAN RESOURCES
MARKETING
PURCHASING
RESEARCH & DEVELOPMENT
SALES
TECHNOLOGY

NUMBER OF VACANCIES
250+ graduate jobs

LOCATIONS OF VACANCIES

STARTING SALARY FOR 2020
£28,250+

UNIVERSITY VISITS IN 2019-20
ASTON, BIRMINGHAM, BRISTOL,
CARDIFF, ESSEX, IMPERIAL COLLEGE
LONDON, MANCHESTER, NOTTINGHAM,
STRATHCLYDE, WARWICK
Please check with your university careers service for full details of local events.

MINIMUM ENTRY REQUIREMENTS
2.1 Degree

APPLICATION DEADLINE
Varies by function

FURTHER INFORMATION
www.Top100GraduateEmployers.com
Register now for the latest news, campus events, work experience and graduate vacancies at BT.

Imagination Required

We don't say this often, but put down your phone for a moment. Now, just try to imagine not being able to surf the web at any time of day or night. Imagine not being able to speak to a friend or relative anywhere in the world with just a device that you carry around in your pocket. Imagine not having hundreds of television channels at your fingertips, or not being able to send photographs to friends in just a few seconds. Imagine what that would feel like... Takes a bit of thinking about, doesn't it?

So, imagine a career with a company that makes all these things happen, as well as many more innovations that we now all take so much for granted. Just imagine changing the world!

At BT we don't offer an ordinary career. We don't offer run of the mill, routine or commonplace. We prefer to feed your creativity – encouraging and empowering you to contribute to a global communications technology business. We've a history that's been driving innovation for over 170 years, constantly developing and evolving. We're a business that millions of people rely on every single day to live their lives and run their businesses. Our services and solutions power industry, fuel innovation, deliver information and opinion across the world, and help find something relaxing to watch at the end of a long day.

We've opportunities for graduates all across our business. Visit us online to start your BT journey, and bring your imagination to life.

Be part of progress.

www.btplc.com/careercentre/earlycareers

GRADUATE VACANCIES IN 2020

FINANCE
GENERAL MANAGEMENT
HUMAN RESOURCES
MARKETING
MEDIA
RESEARCH & DEVELOPMENT
SALES
TECHNOLOGY

NUMBER OF VACANCIES
150 graduate jobs

LOCATIONS OF VACANCIES

Charityworks is the UK non-profit sector's graduate scheme, recruiting around 150 graduates each year. It's a 12-month, paid full-time job in a partner charity or housing association and an acclaimed leadership programme, introducing graduates to what they need to work and lead in the non-profit sector.

Graduates could be providing vital business support and evaluation at a national charity like NSPCC, leading on the improvement of infrastructure projects with a major housing charity, driving business with a large mental health organisation like Mind, or serving a community in a local project. Wherever they're based, they'll have a chance to make a real impact through their work.

Alongside the placement, graduates will take part in a leadership development programme. They'll be matched with an external mentor in the sector to help them make the most of the year. Twice a month they'll come together with their fellow trainees and leaders across the sector to explore and debate the key issues affecting their work and society as a whole and grow in their leadership ability. Graduates will also produce their own research, helping to raise their profile and develop their understanding of their environment.

At the end of the 12-month scheme they will have the experience and skills to kick-start a professional career in the UK non-profit sector and beyond. Charityworks graduates are highly desired, with 98% securing employment within three months if they were looking for it. Typically, over 66% of graduates stay in their host organisations at the end of the year, and 96% of graduates since 2009 have remained within the non-profit or public sector – some have even gone on to start their own organisations.

Whatever graduates want to do in the long-term, Charityworks is a fantastic way to launch their career and change the world for a living.

STARTING SALARY FOR 2020
£18,300
£21,300 for graduates working in London.

UNIVERSITY VISITS IN 2019-20
BIRMINGHAM, BRADFORD, BRISTOL, BRUNEL, CAMBRIDGE, CARDIFF, DURHAM, EDINBURGH, EXETER, GLASGOW, KING'S COLLEGE LONDON, KENT, LANCASTER, LEEDS, LEICESTER, LIVERPOOL, LONDON SCHOOL OF ECONOMICS, MANCHESTER, NEWCASTLE, NORTHUMBRIA, NOTTINGHAM, NOTTINGHAM TRENT, OXFORD, QUEEN MARY LONDON, READING, ROYAL HOLLOWAY, SCHOOL OF AFRICAN STUDIES, SHEFFIELD, SUSSEX, UEA, UNIVERSITY COLLEGE LONDON, WARWICK, YORK
Please check with your university careers service for full details of local events.

MINIMUM ENTRY REQUIREMENTS
2.1 Degree

APPLICATION DEADLINE
February 2020

FURTHER INFORMATION
www.Top100GraduateEmployers.com
Register now for the latest news, campus events, work experience and graduate vacancies at Charityworks.

POVERTY.
AFFORDABLE HOUSING.
DOMESTIC VIOLENCE.
CLIMATE CHANGE.
SOCIAL CARE.

WHAT ROLE WILL YOU PLAY?

Charityworks.
Change the world
for a living.

charity
works •••••
careers that make a difference

Charityworks; Registered Charity No. 1136964, Company No. 7304744

Civil Service
Fast Stream

The Civil Service supports the government of the day to implement its policies effectively. The award-winning Fast Stream is the leadership programme that develops the highest potential graduates to become the future leaders of the Civil Service, offering the opportunity to make a difference to society.

Fast Streamers help to shape the decisions that will affect everyone's lives and to deliver the public services that everyone relies on.

The Fast Stream offers a choice of 15 different schemes, each with high-quality, structured learning and a career path with a government profession. Different schemes provide options to fit a range of circumstances. Several offer the opportunity to study for a professional qualification. Most provide a series of postings with different government departments, at rotating locations. Some provide a more immersive experience with greater flexibility about postings and rotations. Regardless of the degree subject studied, graduates will find that they qualify for most schemes.

Fast Streamers benefit from flexible working arrangements, creating space to achieve life-work balance. Vibrant face-to-face and virtual networks create social opportunities around work, including sporting activities, special interest groups and events. The community actively supports one another, and life-long friendships are frequently formed.

As well as offering a competitive graduate starting salary, the programme offers salary progression on the scheme and excellent earnings potential on completion.

There is no typical Fast Streamer. With no upper age limit to its schemes, people from all ages, cultures and backgrounds thrive on the programme. With unlimited career potential to the very highest levels of the Civil Service, the Fast Stream is the first choice of graduates seeking a rewarding career.

GRADUATE VACANCIES IN 2020

ENGINEERING
FINANCE
GENERAL MANAGEMENT
HUMAN RESOURCES
MARKETING
PURCHASING
RESEARCH & DEVELOPMENT
TECHNOLOGY

NUMBER OF VACANCIES
1,200 graduate jobs

LOCATIONS OF VACANCIES

STARTING SALARY FOR 2020
£28,000

UNIVERSITY VISITS IN 2019-20
ABERYSTWYTH, ASTON, BIRMINGHAM, BRADFORD, BRISTOL, BRUNEL, CARDIFF, CITY, DURHAM, EDINBURGH, ESSEX, EXETER, GLASGOW, HULL, IMPERIAL COLLEGE LONDON, KING'S COLLEGE LONDON, KENT, LANCASTER, LEEDS, LEICESTER, LIVERPOOL, LONDON SCHOOL OF ECONOMICS, MANCHESTER, NEWCASTLE, NORTHUMBRIA, NOTTINGHAM, NOTTINGHAM TRENT, PLYMOUTH, QUEEN MARY LONDON, READING, ROYAL HOLLOWAY, SCHOOL OF AFRICAN STUDIES, SHEFFIELD, SOUTHAMPTON, SUSSEX, UNIVERSITY COLLEGE LONDON, WARWICK, YORK
Please check with your university careers service for full details of local events.

MINIMUM ENTRY REQUIREMENTS
2.2 Degree

APPLICATION DEADLINE
Late October 2019

FURTHER INFORMATION
www.Top100GraduateEmployers.com
*Register now for the latest news, campus events, work experience and graduate vacancies at the **Civil Service Fast Stream**.*

Civil Service
Fast Stream

Be Yourself
Define Your Future
Be a Fast Streamer

Regardless of the degree subject
you studied, our programme offers
the widest choice of professions.

faststream.gov.uk

THE TIMES
TOP 100
GRADUATE EMPLOYERS

GRADUATE EMPLOYER
OF THE YEAR 2019

C/M/S/

CMS is a future-facing law firm combining top quality sector expertise with international scale and a strategy to become a progressive technology-driven firm. The firm focuses on delivering rewarding futures for its clients, its communities and its people.

CMS is a global law firm well equipped to help clients confront challenges and seize opportunities with confidence. CMS put the interests of clients at the heart of everything they do across their 70+ offices in 40+ countries in the UK, Europe, the Middle East, Asia and South America. With more than 1,000 partners and 4,500 lawyers, CMS work in cross-border teams to deliver top quality, practical advice no matter how complex the situation.

The firm is recognised for its sector excellence and focus in consumer products; energy; financial services; hotels & leisure, infrastructure & project finance; life sciences & healthcare; real estate; and technology, media & communications. Their legal expertise is therefore matched by real world, commercial understanding of the markets in which their clients operate.

As a future-facing firm, they embrace technology and are committed to new ideas that challenge conventional ways of doing things if a better solution for clients can be found. Their aim is to anticipate and create sustainable and rewarding futures for their clients, people, and communities.

Keen intellect is vital, but CMS are looking for much more than academic qualifications. Whether applicants are law or non-law students, or if they are looking for a career change, there are several qualities CMS look for in their future trainees. These include personal effectiveness, professional communication, drive for achievement, having a future-facing outlook, leading self and others, ability to build relationships and commercial awareness.

GRADUATE VACANCIES IN 2020

LAW

NUMBER OF VACANCIES
65+ graduate jobs
For training contracts starting in 2021 and 2022.

LOCATIONS OF VACANCIES

STARTING SALARY FOR 2020
£25,000-£43,000
Location dependant.

UNIVERSITY VISITS IN 2019-20
ABERDEEN, BIRMINGHAM, BRISTOL, CAMBRIDGE, CARDIFF, DUNDEE, DURHAM, EDINBURGH, EXETER, GLASGOW, IMPERIAL COLLEGE LONDON, KING'S COLLEGE LONDON, LONDON SCHOOL OF ECONOMICS, MANCHESTER, NEWCASTLE, NOTTINGHAM, OXFORD, QUEEN MARY LONDON, SHEFFIELD, STRATHCLYDE, UNIVERSITY COLLEGE LONDON, WARWICK, YORK
Please check with your university careers service for full details of local events.

MINIMUM ENTRY REQUIREMENTS
2.1 Degree
128 UCAS points
320 UCAS points for those who passed exams before 2017.

APPLICATION DEADLINE
January 2020

FURTHER INFORMATION
www.Top100GraduateEmployers.com
Register now for the latest news, campus events, work experience and graduate vacancies at CMS.

deloitte.co.uk/careers

facebook.com/DeloitteCareersUK **f**
linkedin.com/company/deloitte-uk **in**   twitter.com/DeloitteCareers **y**
instagram.com/DeloitteCareersUK **O**   youtube.com/DeloitteCareersUK **▶**

Deloitte.

GRADUATE VACANCIES IN 2020
ACCOUNTANCY
CONSULTING
FINANCE
HUMAN RESOURCES
LAW
PROPERTY
TECHNOLOGY

NUMBER OF VACANCIES
1,000+ graduate jobs

LOCATIONS OF VACANCIES

STARTING SALARY FOR 2020
£Competitive

UNIVERSITY VISITS IN 2019-20
ABERDEEN, ASTON, BATH, BIRMINGHAM,
BRISTOL, CAMBRIDGE, CARDIFF, CITY,
DURHAM, EDINBURGH, EXETER, GLASGOW,
IMPERIAL COLLEGE LONDON, KING'S
COLLEGE LONDON, LANCASTER, LEEDS,
LEICESTER, LIVERPOOL, LONDON SCHOOL OF
ECONOMICS, LOUGHBOROUGH, MANCHESTER,
NEWCASTLE, NOTTINGHAM, OXFORD, QUEEN
MARY LONDON, READING, SHEFFIELD,
SOUTHAMPTON, ST ANDREWS, STRATHCLYDE,
SURREY, UEA, ULSTER, UNIVERSITY COLLEGE
LONDON, WARWICK, YORK
*Please check with your university careers
service for full details of local events.*

MINIMUM ENTRY REQUIREMENTS
2.1 Degree
104 UCAS points
*260 UCAS points for those who passed
exams before 2017.*

APPLICATION DEADLINE
See website for details.

FURTHER INFORMATION
www.Top100GraduateEmployers.com
*Register now for the latest news, campus
events, work experience and graduate
vacancies at **Deloitte**.*

**Deloitte is a business that doesn't just recognise the need to
remain curious, but fully embraces it. At Deloitte, graduates
follow a career path that enables them to be true to themselves.
To dream bigger, think creatively and deliver real impact.
Deloitte is reshaping both the business and technology world.**

In this ever more complex world, it's the smartest and most curious people
that make the difference, because they're driven by imagination and the desire
to add value. Deloitte is a business that doesn't just recognise the need to
remain curious, but fully embraces it. Here, graduates will follow a career path
that enables them to be true to themselves. To dream bigger, think creatively
and deliver real impact. This is a place for go-getters, problem solvers, those
who want to make a difference.

Deloitte is reshaping both the business and technology landscape. From
human capital, tax consulting and legal to technology and cyber, they're
delivering end-to-end improvement programmes, turning disruption into
opportunity, and redesigning the art of Audit through automation.

It's not the background or experience of graduates that matters most, it's
their mind, and how they'll use it to make an impact for clients, as well as their
own career. Deloitte has opportunities across their entire business, so whatever
their passion, graduates will find something that's right for them.

Deloitte have 29 offices across the UK and Northern Ireland, including
Aberdeen, Belfast, Cardiff, Channel Islands, Gatwick, London, Manchester,
Reading, St Albans and many more. Whichever location is chosen, graduates
can be sure of joining a business that is both local and global, with networks,
connections and values that reach right across the world.

This is the home of the imaginative – be part of it.

Deloitte.

Where are solutions before they're found?

Welcome to the home of the curious.
A place for those who know that imagination, ingenuity and solution finding are what humans are made of. We offer life-changing careers and professional qualifications, across all industries, to those who are true to themselves. Those who set no limits to their dreams and ambitions.

deloitte.co.uk/careers
What impact will you make?

DLA PIPER

dlapipergraduates.com

graduaterecruitment@dlapiper.com ✉

twitter.com/DLA_Piper_grads 🐦 facebook.com/DLAPiperGrads f

DLA Piper is one of the world's leading business law firms. With over 90 offices in more than 40 countries, the firm provides seamless local and cross-border advice. The firm believes great businesses can make a better world. That's why, every day, DLA Piper helps its clients succeed.

DLA Piper's progressive mindset challenges conventions and evolves its global legal offering into broader advisory services and new business areas. Through the firm's deep industry knowledge, technological solutions, and diversity of thought and experience, clients embrace change and seize opportunities.

DLA Piper's ten sector groups cover the full range of business law services. Clients include multinationals, startups, public sector bodies and governments. Across the two leading legal directories, the firm has over 1,900 lawyer rankings, and over 900 practice group/sector rankings. Through its global nonprofit initiative, the firm contributed over 200,000 pro bono hours in 2018 alone and has also pledged $6.5 million to UNICEF to improve child justice.

The firm's entrepreneurial and supportive culture promotes bold, ambitious thinking and a warm, empathetic approach. Trusting, collaborative relationships with clients and each other are at the heart of everything it does.

DLA Piper is looking for ambitious, capable and forward-thinking graduates from any degree discipline to join its journey. Graduates will be based in one of the firm's seven UK offices: Birmingham, Edinburgh, Leeds, Liverpool, London, Manchester or Sheffield.

During their two-year training contract, graduates will complete four six-month rotations, and the majority will undertake an international or client secondment. As part of DLA Piper's future, all graduates are given the resources and opportunities to build an exciting, fulfilling career.

GRADUATE VACANCIES IN 2020
LAW

NUMBER OF VACANCIES
65-70 graduate jobs
For training contracts starting in 2022.

LOCATIONS OF VACANCIES

Vacancies also available in Asia and elsewhere in the world.

STARTING SALARY FOR 2020
£45,000
London salary. £28,000 in other offices.

UNIVERSITY VISITS IN 2019-20
ABERDEEN, BIRMINGHAM, BRISTOL, CAMBRIDGE, DUNDEE, DURHAM, EDINBURGH, GLASGOW, KING'S COLLEGE LONDON, LANCASTER, LEEDS, LEICESTER, LIVERPOOL, LONDON SCHOOL OF ECONOMICS, MANCHESTER, NEWCASTLE, NOTTINGHAM, OXFORD, QUEEN MARY LONDON, SHEFFIELD, ST ANDREWS, STRATHCLYDE, UNIVERSITY COLLEGE LONDON, WARWICK, YORK
Please check with your university careers service for full details of local events.

MINIMUM ENTRY REQUIREMENTS
2.1 Degree
128 UCAS points
320 UCAS points for those who passed exams before 2017.

APPLICATION DEADLINE
November-December 2019
November for Training Contracts, December for Summer Internships.

FURTHER INFORMATION
www.Top100GraduateEmployers.com
Register now for the latest news, campus events, work experience and graduate vacancies at DLA Piper.

SHARE OUR VISION
SHAPE YOUR FUTURE

Our goal is simple. We want to create the future leaders
of the firm. That means giving you the skills you need to
become a successful lawyer, but also the experiences
to discover where your true interests lie.

Find out more at
DLAPIPERGRADUATES.COM

GRADUATE VACANCIES IN 2020

ENGINEERING

FINANCE

MARKETING

TECHNOLOGY

NUMBER OF VACANCIES
75-100 graduate jobs

LOCATIONS OF VACANCIES

Vacancies also available in Asia.

STARTING SALARY FOR 2020
£29,000

UNIVERSITY VISITS IN 2019-20
BATH, BRISTOL, EXETER, IMPERIAL
COLLEGE, LEEDS, LOUGHBOROUGH,
NOTTINGHAM, SHEFFIELD,
SOUTHAMPTON, WARWICK
Please check with your university careers service for full details of local events.

MINIMUM ENTRY REQUIREMENTS
2.1 Degree
Relevant degree required for some roles.

APPLICATION DEADLINE
Varies by function

FURTHER INFORMATION
www.Top100GraduateEmployers.com
Register now for the latest news, campus events, work experience and graduate vacancies at Dyson.

Dyson is transforming globally. In 2012 they were just 3,120 people – today they're over 12,000. With ever expanding interests from personal care to electric vehicles, they are on the lookout for people who have a passion for solving problems that can contribute to the future of cutting-edge technology.

Since its early success Dyson has always gone against the grain and carved out its own path, from bagless vacuums to bladeless fans, revolutionary hairdryers to building its own degree. Whether an intern, graduate or industry leader at Dyson, they all share the same values. It's helped them to stick to their roots, build the technologies they have today and bolster the ones they're creating for tomorrow.

Dyson graduates are problem solvers and quick thinkers who have insatiable curiosity and the ability to look at things in a different way. With a mission-based approach to work, they gain invaluable exposure to the inner workings at Dyson through tough projects with real challenges and real responsibility. Whether they are joining the engineering, commercial or support teams, Dyson graduates work alongside industry experts, with exposure to senior leaders. They don't just learn how things are done – they find ways to make them better.

In addition to a stimulating work environment, there's plenty going on outside of the office too. With an on-site gym, two large cafes and plenty of nature walks, it's a fulfilling place to start working life within a community of people who inspire each other. They're on the lookout for graduates to join teams across marketing, engineering and more. People who share Dyson's core values and a passion for technology, those who won't settle for 'good enough' and can push the boundaries without fear.

Inquisitive minds.
Disruptive technology.
Endless opportunity.

careers.dyson.com/early-careers

Enterprise started life as a small business. Now it's grown to be the largest global mobility provider in the world, with 10,000+ branches globally, an annual turnover of more than $24 billion and the biggest rental vehicle fleet on the planet. Join them and be one of the people driving this success.

From their senior leaders to their apprentices, Enterprise gives everyone the freedom to explore their potential, and the opportunities they need to rise to new challenges and take their skills to the next level – because their growth is what makes Enterprise's growth possible.

Nowhere is this philosophy better illustrated than in their approach to graduate careers. When people join their award-winning Management Training Programme, they empower them to start contributing right from the word go. It helps that they are divided up into smaller, local branches, so their graduates can gain experience of running their own business in as little as two years.

As a Times Top 50 Employer for Women for 14 years running, Enterprise has created a work environment where women can thrive, and they're proud to be helping women break all kinds of stereotypes. With the support of both management and their peers, women joining Enterprise are encouraged to rise to new levels in their career. From mentoring to flexibility for major life events like maternity leave, they ensure that women have what they need to succeed.

The other great thing about Enterprise is that they're still family-owned. This allows them to look forward even more confidently to the future, providing the stability they need to pursue the long-term good for their customers, their business and their employees. Join Enterprise on their Graduate Programme, and become one of the new generation helping them write the next chapter of their success story.

GRADUATE VACANCIES IN 2020
GENERAL MANAGEMENT
RETAILING
SALES

NUMBER OF VACANCIES
900+ graduate jobs

LOCATIONS OF VACANCIES

STARTING SALARY FOR 2020
£21,000
Plus performance-based bonuses once the graduate programme has been completed, and location allowance if applicable.

UNIVERSITY VISITS IN 2019-20
ABERDEEN, ABERYSTWYTH, ASTON, BANGOR, BATH, BELFAST, BIRMINGHAM, BRADFORD, BRISTOL, BRUNEL, CARDIFF, CITY, DUNDEE, DURHAM, ESSEX, EXETER, GLASGOW, HERIOT-WATT, HULL, KEELE, KENT, LANCASTER, LEEDS, LEICESTER, LIVERPOOL, LOUGHBOROUGH, MANCHESTER, NEWCASTLE, NORTHUMBRIA, NOTTINGHAM, NOTTINGHAM TRENT, OXFORD BROOKES, PLYMOUTH, READING, ROYAL HOLLOWAY, SHEFFIELD, SOUTHAMPTON, STIRLING, STRATHCLYDE, SURREY, SUSSEX, SWANSEA, UEA, ULSTER, WARWICK, YORK
Please check with your university careers service for full details of local events.

APPLICATION DEADLINE
Year-round recruitment

FURTHER INFORMATION
www.Top100GraduateEmployers.com
Register now for the latest news, campus events, work experience and graduate vacancies at Enterprise Rent-A-Car.

Your prospects

Do wonders for them as an
Intern or **Management Trainee**

What does a graduate career with the world's largest car rental company look like? It starts in one of our 10,000 branches worldwide. It continues with you becoming a manager of one of those branches, in as little as two years' time. From there, you can go in whatever direction you choose. National sales? Business rental? Human resources? International opportunities? The choice is yours. And whether you join us on our award-winning Management Trainee program or as an Intern, you'll enjoy great benefits, excellent training and real responsibility from day one.

Discover more at
careers.enterprise.co.uk

ExxonMobil

Imagine working for the world's largest publicly traded oil and gas company, on tasks that affect nearly everyone in the world today and for future generations to come. ExxonMobil in the UK is better known for its Esso and Mobil brands due to the success of its service stations and high performance lubricants.

ExxonMobil offers challenging long-term careers to high performing graduates, as well as summer and year placements with real responsibility!

There's no such thing as an average day at ExxonMobil and there are many different career paths available from a technical career to a leadership position to a commercial role. For graduates who are looking for a long-term career that will be challenging, rewarding and certainly varied, then a career with ExxonMobil might just be for them.

What are ExxonMobil looking for? For the technical schemes, applications are welcomed from Chemical, Electrical and Mechanical (and related) Engineers with a 2:1 minimum. For the commercial schemes, applications from a number of disciplines including Science/Engineering/IT/Business degrees with a 2:1 minimum are accepted.

In addition to the competitive base salary and relocation allowance, employees are also offered a matched 2-for-1 share scheme, final salary pension plan, private health care scheme, 33 days holiday per annum (including public holidays), interest-free loan, tailored graduate training and continuous development, support towards studying for professional qualifications such as IChemE, free sports facilities and subsidised dining facilities at most locations, voluntary community activities, international opportunities and regular job rotations (typically every one to three years) with opportunities to develop and hone skills.

GRADUATE VACANCIES IN 2020

ENGINEERING
HUMAN RESOURCES
MARKETING

NUMBER OF VACANCIES
30+ graduate jobs

LOCATIONS OF VACANCIES

STARTING SALARY FOR 2020
£Competitive

UNIVERSITY VISITS IN 2019-20
BATH, BIRMINGHAM, BRISTOL, CAMBRIDGE, EDINBURGH, IMPERIAL COLLEGE LONDON, LEEDS, LOUGHBOROUGH, MANCHESTER, NEWCASTLE, NOTTINGHAM, SHEFFIELD, SOUTHAMPTON, STRATHCLYDE, UNIVERSITY COLLEGE LONDON
Please check with your university careers service for full details of local events.

MINIMUM ENTRY REQUIREMENTS
2.1 Degree

APPLICATION DEADLINE
Autumn 2019

FURTHER INFORMATION
www.Top100GraduateEmployers.com
Register now for the latest news, campus events, work experience and graduate vacancies at ExxonMobil.

ExxonMobil

Be a part
of our energy.

At ExxonMobil we're using technology and innovation to
meet the world's growing energy needs. We're recruiting
now for exceptional people who we can empower to think
independently, take initiative and be innovative.

**Find out more about our exciting
opportunities at jobs.exxonmobil.com**

Energy lives here™

FRONTLINE

CHANGING LIVES

At least half a million children in England don't have a safe or stable home. These children and their families face some of the worst life chances, but great social work has the power to change this. That's why Frontline recruits and develops outstanding individuals to be social workers and transform the lives of the most vulnerable children and families.

Frontline's two-year Leadership Development programme offers graduates an exciting new route into one of Britain's toughest and most rewarding professions. Frontline prioritise hands-on experience through practice-based learning, and participants will benefit from tailored intensive practical and academic training, as they join a new generation of children's social workers.

Following a five-week residential training programme, participants spend two years working in a local authority children's services department. The first year qualifies participants as social workers through direct work with children and families. In the second year they work as a newly-qualified social worker responsible for their own caseload, and will complete a fully funded master's qualification.

Frontline participants work directly with children, families, schools, courts and the police, to empower families to achieve positive change. They will develop a whole range of invaluable and transferable skills including leadership, relationship-building and conflict resolution. Participants will inspire, persuade and be part of a leadership profession which brings out the best in diverse groups of people. Additionally, participants will benefit from ongoing leadership development coaching.

Joining Frontline provides the opportunity to make a real difference to the lives of vulnerable children and their families. Frontline welcomes applications from students from a range of degree disciplines.

GRADUATE VACANCIES IN 2020
SOCIAL WORK

NUMBER OF VACANCIES
452 graduate jobs

LOCATIONS OF VACANCIES

STARTING SALARY FOR 2020
£18,000-£20,000

UNIVERSITY VISITS IN 2019-20
ASTON, BATH, BIRMINGHAM, BRISTOL, CAMBRIDGE, CARDIFF, DURHAM, EDINBURGH, ESSEX, EXETER, KEELE, KING'S COLLEGE LONDON, KENT, LANCASTER, LEEDS, LEICESTER, LIVERPOOL, LONDON SCHOOL OF ECONOMICS, LOUGHBOROUGH, MANCHESTER, NEWCASTLE, NORTHUMBRIA, NOTTINGHAM, NOTTINGHAM TRENT, OXFORD, QUEEN MARY LONDON, READING, ROYAL HOLLOWAY, SHEFFIELD, SOUTHAMPTON, ST ANDREWS, SURREY, SUSSEX, SWANSEA, UEA, UNIVERSITY COLLEGE LONDON, WARWICK, YORK
Please check with your university careers service for full details of local events.

MINIMUM ENTRY REQUIREMENTS
2.1 Degree

APPLICATION DEADLINE
2nd December 2019

FURTHER INFORMATION
www.Top100GraduateEmployers.com
Register now for the latest news, campus events, work experience and graduate vacancies at Frontline.

RULE BREAKER
RISK TAKER
DEAL MAKER

BE THE DIFFERENCE

There's no rule book that tells you what to do in every situation. That's why Frontline's two-year leadership development programme teaches you to innovate and adapt, with training in the field. Earn up to a £20k bursary in your first year while you train, and up to a £34k salary in your second as a qualified social worker.

THEFRONTLINE.ORG.UK/BE-THE-DIFFERENCE

FRONTLINE

Leadership Development Programme
Children's Social Work

CHANGING LIVES

gchq-careers.co.uk
instagram.com/GCHQ 　twitter.com/GCHQ

GCHQ, Britain's signals intelligence agency, plays a major role in protecting the country's people, businesses and infrastructure. Think terrorism, espionage, organised crime and cyber attacks. Using technical expertise and intelligence to counter these threats, graduates can expect a truly fascinating career.

As Britain faces increasingly sophisticated threats, GCHQ constantly develops unique and creative solutions to stay one step ahead of adversaries. GCHQ intelligence helps keep British forces safe, prevents terrorism, crime and protects Britain against cyber attacks.

GCHQ has a diverse workforce and is looking for graduates with different skills, backgrounds and perspectives to share its commitment to keeping Britain safe, secure and successful. Graduates joining GCHQ can expect challenging projects, early responsibility, outstanding professional development and a rewarding career experience.

GCHQ is proud of its mission and its people. Its working culture encourages open minds and attitudes and is supported by a welfare and benefits structure that enables its workforce to be at its best. From extensive training and development that enables employees to expand their skills, to the flexibility to explore different roles, tools and technologies, a career at GCHQ offers graduates a unique opportunity and supports them to achieve their full potential.

Graduate careers are varied, including technology, analysis, and languages, as well as corporate roles including project management, finance and procurement. Students can take advantage of a variety of summer placements, including Languages and Maths, as well as a Cyber Summer School. Bursaries are also offered to those who plan to, or already study a STEM subject at university.

Due to the sensitive nature of the work applicants must be British citizens.

GRADUATE VACANCIES IN 2020
ENGINEERING
GENERAL MANAGEMENT
RESEARCH & DEVELOPMENT
TECHNOLOGY

NUMBER OF VACANCIES
150+ graduate jobs

LOCATIONS OF VACANCIES

STARTING SALARY FOR 2020
£27,000+

UNIVERSITY VISITS IN 2019-20
BATH, BIRMINGHAM, BRADFORD, BRISTOL, CAMBRIDGE, CARDIFF, DURHAM, EXETER, GLASGOW, HULL, IMPERIAL COLLEGE LONDON, KING'S COLLEGE LONDON, LANCASTER, LEEDS, MANCHESTER, NOTTINGHAM, OXFORD, ROYAL HOLLOWAY, SHEFFIELD, UNIVERSITY COLLEGE LONDON, WARWICK, YORK
Please check with your university careers service for full details of local events.

MINIMUM ENTRY REQUIREMENTS
2.2 Degree

APPLICATION DEADLINE
Varies by function

FURTHER INFORMATION
www.Top100GraduateEmployers.com
Register now for the latest news, campus events, work experience and graduate vacancies at GCHQ.

HARK

"You don't need to know much about accounting and finance. If you're willing to learn and have got the right attitude, we'll teach you everything you need to know."

**Public Sector Trainee
Birmingham**

Grant Thornton is one of the world's leading independent assurance, tax and advisory firms. They are driven by independent thinkers that provide high quality business and financial advice to a wide range of clients in countries all over the world. Shape more than just your career at Grant Thornton.

In Grant Thornton's graduate programme, graduates get the training and support to help them grow in confidence and to develop the skills they need to become a future leader. But they'll also do so much more than that. With a relentless focus on quality and integrity, graduates will help businesses to achieve their objectives and flourish.

Graduates join a three-year programme to become professionally qualified advisers, specialising in either advisory, audit or tax. In this training programme, they'll get hands-on experience working with clients, from multinationals to start-ups, across public and private sectors.

Grant Thornton's graduate programme is just the beginning. Once graduates get their qualification, all kinds of career routes will open up to them, from audit, tax and advisory to people management and business development. What happens next and how fast they progress is up to them. Grant Thornton has a flexible approach to academic entry requirements. The firm will consider applicants' academic achievements, but their strengths, motivations and connection with the business and its values are more important.

They are looking for people with a broad range of interests and experiences. Grant Thornton does things differently. They give their people the freedom to drive change and shape their own destinies. Their people are inspired to make a difference. Their collaborative culture means they share ideas as well as the responsibility for making them happen.

GRADUATE VACANCIES IN 2020
ACCOUNTANCY

NUMBER OF VACANCIES
400-450 graduate jobs

LOCATIONS OF VACANCIES

STARTING SALARY FOR 2020
£Competitive

UNIVERSITY VISITS IN 2019-20
ASTON, BATH, BIRMINGHAM, BRISTOL, CAMBRIDGE, CARDIFF, CITY, DURHAM, EDINBURGH, EXETER, GLASGOW, HERIOT-WATT, KING'S COLLEGE LONDON, KENT, LEEDS, LEICESTER, LIVERPOOL, LOUGHBOROUGH, MANCHESTER, NEWCASTLE, NOTTINGHAM, NOTTINGHAM TRENT, OXFORD BROOKES, QUEEN MARY LONDON, READING, SHEFFIELD, SOUTHAMPTON, STIRLING, STRATHCLYDE, SURREY, UNIVERSITY COLLEGE LONDON, WARWICK, YORK
Please check with your university careers service for full details of local events.

APPLICATION DEADLINE
Year-round recruitment

FURTHER INFORMATION
www.Top100GraduateEmployers.com
Register now for the latest news, campus events, work experience and graduate vacancies at Grant Thornton.

Build
for
everyone

Together, we can
create opportunities
for people to learn, be
heard, and succeed.
google.com/students

Google

SHAPE MORE THAN JUST YOUR CAREER

At Grant Thornton we have a unique culture where thinking differently is encouraged, your opinions are heard and your contributions are valued. Our people are given the freedom to drive change and shape their own destinies. So if you'd like to make a difference, bring your passion, ambitions and inspiration, and together let's make it happen.

trainees.grantthornton.co.uk

 Grant Thornton

An instinct for growth™

careers.herbertsmithfreehills.com/uk/grads

graduatesUK@hsf.com

twitter.com/HSFgraduatesUK
facebook.com/HSFgraduatesUK
instagram.com/HSFgraduatesUK
linkedin.com/company/herbert-smith-freehills

HERBERT SMITH FREEHILLS

Herbert Smith Freehills is a leading, full-service international law firm that works on some of the most important cases and deals for the world's biggest organisations. As the world continues to evolve at an unprecedented pace, they are continuing to build an organisation ready for tomorrow.

Defined by their inclusive culture and commitment to innovation, Herbert Smith Freehills give trainees the platform and responsibility to make an impact from day one. They are inviting graduates to build a career, help lead them into tomorrow, and shape the industry's future.

No other firm has more Chambers rankings, and few operate at the forefront of so many exciting sectors. With over 3,000 lawyers in 27 international offices, their leading international teams include an award-winning in-house advocacy unit and dispute resolution team, which is recognised as number one globally.

That exceptional performance is due to innovation being at the heart of everything they do. At Herbert Smith Freehills, it's less about being ready for the future and more about being ready to lead it. That means everyone is expected to bring new ideas to the work they do and how they do it. All lawyers, including graduates, harness the latest technology to drive better outcomes and have the platform to drive and deliver innovations that bring the future of law to life.

Trainees are a part of making that future happen. All trainees tailor their training contracts and sit in a broad range of practice groups, including the firm's leading corporate and disputes teams. They are given real responsibility across both fee-earning work and pro bono initiatives. Here, trainees get the essential combination of a global and progressive approach that provides a true insight into the future of law and a platform to shape their place in it.

GRADUATE VACANCIES IN 2020
LAW

NUMBER OF VACANCIES
Up to 60 graduate jobs
For training contracts starting in 2022.

LOCATIONS OF VACANCIES

STARTING SALARY FOR 2020
£45,000

UNIVERSITY VISITS IN 2019-20
BATH, BELFAST, BIRMINGHAM, BRISTOL, CAMBRIDGE, CARDIFF, DUNDEE, DURHAM, EDINBURGH, EXETER, GLASGOW, KING'S COLLEGE LONDON, KENT, LANCASTER, LEEDS, LEICESTER, LONDON SCHOOL OF ECONOMICS, MANCHESTER, NEWCASTLE, NOTTINGHAM, OXFORD, QUEEN MARY LONDON, SCHOOL OF AFRICAN STUDIES, SHEFFIELD, SOUTHAMPTON, SUSSEX, UEA, UNIVERSITY COLLEGE LONDON, WARWICK, YORK
Please check with your university careers service for full details of local events.

MINIMUM ENTRY REQUIREMENTS
2.1 Degree
Mitigating circumstances are taken into consideration.

APPLICATION DEADLINE
18th December 2019
For spring and summer vacation schemes. See website for other deadlines.

FURTHER INFORMATION
www.Top100GraduateEmployers.com
*Register now for the latest news, campus events, work experience and graduate vacancies at **Herbert Smith Freehills**.*

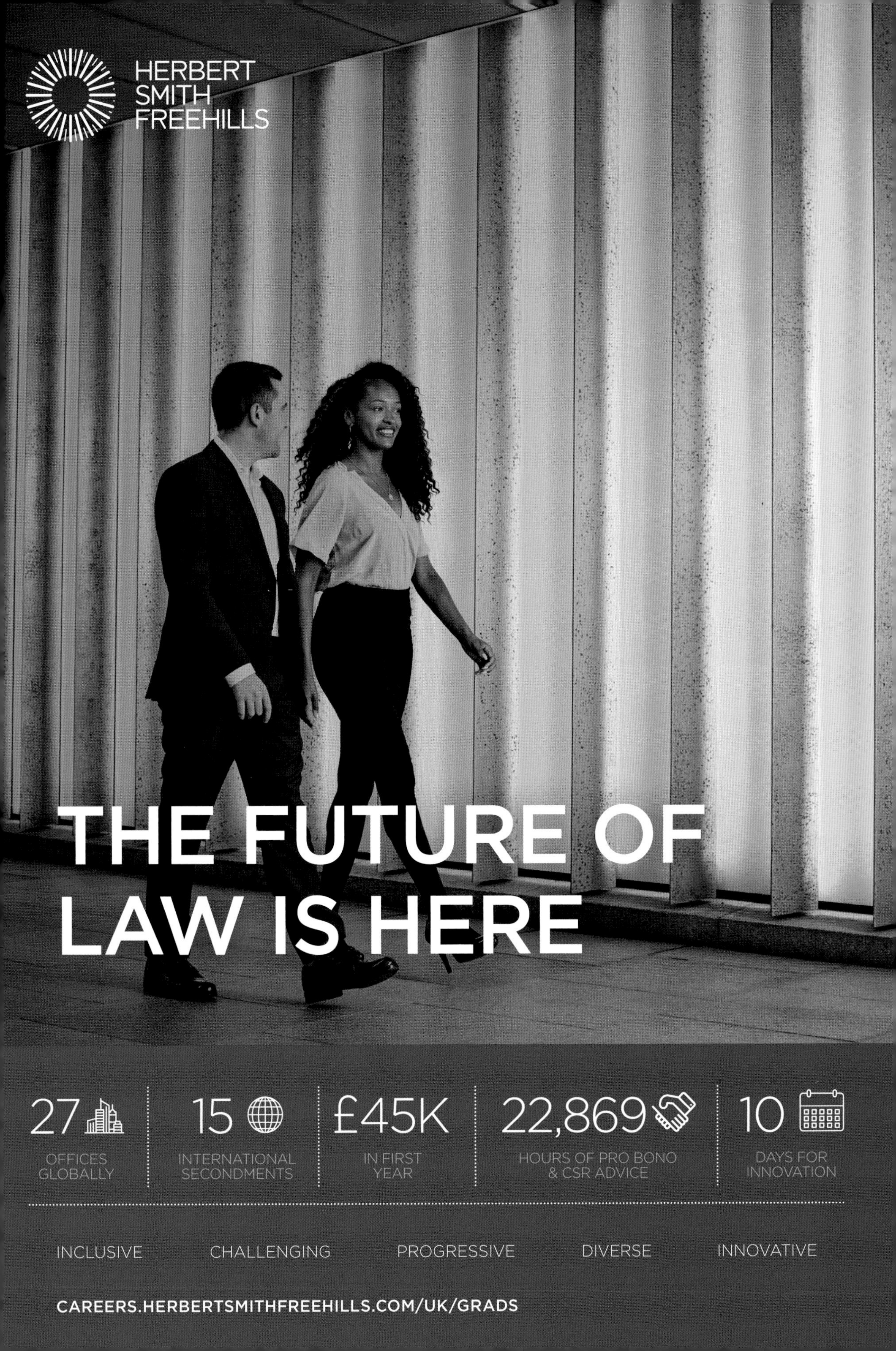

HERBERT
SMITH
FREEHILLS

THE FUTURE OF
LAW IS HERE

27
OFFICES
GLOBALLY

15
INTERNATIONAL
SECONDMENTS

£45K
IN FIRST
YEAR

22,869
HOURS OF PRO BONO
& CSR ADVICE

10
DAYS FOR
INNOVATION

INCLUSIVE   CHALLENGING   PROGRESSIVE   DIVERSE   INNOVATIVE

CAREERS.HERBERTSMITHFREEHILLS.COM/UK/GRADS

graduate.recruitment@hoganlovells.com ✉

twitter.com/HLGraduatesUK 𝕏   facebook.com/HoganLovellsGradsUK f
instagram.com/HoganLovellsGradsUK 📷   linkedin.com/company/hoganlovells in

Hogan Lovells

GRADUATE VACANCIES IN 2020
LAW

NUMBER OF VACANCIES
50 graduate jobs
For training contracts starting in 2022.

LOCATIONS OF VACANCIES

STARTING SALARY FOR 2020
£46,000

UNIVERSITY VISITS IN 2019-20
BATH, BIRMINGHAM, BRISTOL, CAMBRIDGE, CARDIFF, TRINITY COLLEGE DUBLIN, DURHAM, EXETER, IMPERIAL COLLEGE LONDON, KING'S COLLEGE LONDON, LEEDS, LEICESTER, LIVERPOOL, LONDON SCHOOL OF ECONOMICS, LOUGHBOROUGH, MANCHESTER, NEWCASTLE, NOTTINGHAM, OXFORD, QUEEN MARY LONDON, ROYAL HOLLOWAY, UNIVERSITY COLLEGE LONDON, WARWICK, YORK
Please check with your university careers service for full details of local events.

MINIMUM ENTRY REQUIREMENTS
2.1 Degree

APPLICATION DEADLINE
Law: 31st July 2020
Non-law: 31st January 2020

FURTHER INFORMATION
www.Top100GraduateEmployers.com
Register now for the latest news, campus events, work experience and graduate vacancies at Hogan Lovells.

When Hogan Lovells say they're global game-changers, it's no exaggeration. With a network of 2,600+ lawyers in 48 international offices, they solve some of the toughest legal problems around the world. The best part? They do it all as one team, seamlessly, across continents, borders and time zones.

Having this global reach attracts prestigious clients from a wide range of industries. For graduates, that means exposure to exciting, headline-grabbing legal projects which help clients become more innovative.

The two-year training contracts focus on hands-on learning and expert guidance. As a result, graduates develop a deep understanding of the firm's distinctive approach to finding the very best solutions to demanding business challenges.

Here's how it works: graduates do four six-month seats across different practice areas, including corporate, finance, global regulatory, intellectual property and litigation. Plus, for one of those seats, they'll have the chance to apply for an international or client secondment.

Hogan Lovells also run highly regarded summer and winter vacation schemes, which offer the perfect launchpad for legal careers. In fact, around three-quarters of trainee solicitors who join the firm each year have taken part in one. Lasting up to three weeks, these paid schemes see participants work in key practice areas, where they'll take on legal research, go to meetings and, where possible, attend court.

No matter which path they take, graduates will grow their legal expertise, sharpen their commercial edge and tackle fascinating challenges for some of the most well-respected clients across the globe. Furthermore, they'll be part of a close-knit team – with support and encouragement from everyone around them.

Hogan Lovells

Join the
Global Game-Changers

Undergraduate and graduate careers in Law

- £46K starting salary
- 48 global offices
- 2600 lawyers worldwide
- 50 training contracts
- 70 vacation schemes
- 34 FTSE 100 clients

We're a global law firm solving some of the toughest legal problems around the world. It's headline-grabbing work – and we do it seamlessly across industries, borders and time zones. For you, that means exposure to all sorts of exciting legal projects that have international, future-defining impact.

Question is, are you ready to change the game?

Find out more at
hoganlovells.com/graduates

HSBC

With a network of some 3,900 offices in 67 countries and territories, serving around 38 million customers, HSBC is one of the largest global banks. HSBC's purpose is connecting customers to opportunities, enabling businesses and economies to prosper.

HSBC are looking for students and graduates who are collaborative and curious thinkers, with the courage to challenge the status quo and the motivation to make a positive impact for customers worldwide.

HSBC embed sustainability in the way they do business, and are committed to balancing social, environmental and economic considerations in the decisions they make. The bank wants a connected international workforce of unique thinkers that reflects the communities and markets in which they serve. They recognise the importance of having a diverse workforce to meet the needs of their customers. That's why they hire, develop and promote employees based on merit, and provide an open, supportive and inclusive working environment. HSBC is an organisation where everyone can be themselves.

Students and graduates can apply to join internship and graduate programmes across the bank in Commercial Banking, Operations, Technology, Global Banking & Markets, Global Private Banking or Retail Banking & Wealth Management, including Global Asset Management. The journey begins with an induction followed by a number of rotations across the chosen business area. Successful applicants will work with talented colleagues and be supported by mentors and a buddy as they progress. The technical and personal development training ensures graduates are well equipped to achieve their full potential and flourish in their chosen career path, regardless of the degree subject they have studied.

GRADUATE VACANCIES IN 2020

ACCOUNTANCY
FINANCE
GENERAL MANAGEMENT
INVESTMENT BANKING
RETAILING
TECHNOLOGY

NUMBER OF VACANCIES
1,000+ graduate jobs

LOCATIONS OF VACANCIES

Vacancies also available in Europe, the USA, Asia, and elsewhere in the world.

STARTING SALARY FOR 2020
£Competitive
Plus a competitive bonus.

UNIVERSITY VISITS IN 2019-20
ASTON, BATH, BIRMINGHAM, BRISTOL, CAMBRIDGE, TRINITY COLLEGE DUBLIN, DURHAM, EDINBURGH, EXETER, GLASGOW, HERIOT-WATT, IMPERIAL COLLEGE LONDON, KING'S COLLEGE LONDON, LANCASTER, LEEDS, LEICESTER, LIVERPOOL, LONDON SCHOOL OF ECONOMICS, LOUGHBOROUGH, MANCHESTER, NEWCASTLE, NOTTINGHAM, OXFORD, QUEEN MARY LONDON, SHEFFIELD, SOUTHAMPTON, ST ANDREWS, STRATHCLYDE, UEA, UNIVERSITY COLLEGE LONDON, WARWICK
Please check with your university careers service for full details of local events.

MINIMUM ENTRY REQUIREMENTS
2.1 Degree
120 UCAS points
300 UCAS points for those who passed exams before 2017.

APPLICATION DEADLINE
Varies by function

FURTHER INFORMATION
www.Top100GraduateEmployers.com
Register now for the latest news, campus events, work experience and graduate vacancies at HSBC.

We value your courage.
Because we're just as courageous.

At HSBC we encourage all our employees to have the courage to challenge the status quo. Because it's often the people who are bold enough to share and voice their opinions who can change the world for the better.

That's why we're looking for people who think, see and do things differently and who can represent and relate to our diverse global customer base. Regardless of your degree discipline, we have a variety of internship and graduate opportunities across the bank:

- Commercial Banking
- Global Banking and Markets
- Global Private Banking
- Retail Banking and Wealth Management
- Operations
- Technology

So, if you're a courageous mind wanting a career in banking visit hsbc.com/earlycareers

 **HSBC**

Together we thrive

GRADUATE VACANCIES IN 2020

ENGINEERING

RESEARCH & DEVELOPMENT

TECHNOLOGY

NUMBER OF VACANCIES
40-50 graduate jobs

LOCATIONS OF VACANCIES

Huawei is the world's largest telecommunications equipment manufacturer and a leading global provider of information and communications technology (ICT) infrastructure and smart devices, covering cross-telecom networks, IT, smart devices, and cloud services.

Huawei creates lasting value for its customers and colleagues, delivering exciting careers that help to connect more than a third of the people around the world through networks built with its partners. They are committed to bringing digital to every person, home and organisation for a fully connected, intelligent world.

In addition to its Reading headquarters, Huawei operates two joint innovation centres, ten centres of excellence and three R&D centres across the UK. Collectively, these sites employ a total of more than 1,600 people, and each location delivers inspiring opportunities for employees.

Huawei believes in investing in the future of talent in its business, and developing staff through training. It prides itself on offering stimulating opportunities for graduates to grow in their early careers, and hiring the very best through rapidly expanding recruitment programmes.

This year saw Huawei's intake of graduates more than double, and 2020 is set to see a similar expansion, with up to 50 spaces available for university leavers to launch their working lives in a role that will see them rapidly learn and progress in a cutting-edge environment.

Huawei's "Seeds of the Future" programme also offers students the opportunity of a lifetime, providing travel to China and opportunities to develop their science, technology, engineering and mathematics skills – as well as basic Mandarin – in locations like Beijing and Shenzen.

STARTING SALARY FOR 2020
£30,000+

UNIVERSITY VISITS IN 2019-20
BIRMINGHAM, CAMBRIDGE, TRINITY COLLEGE DUBLIN, UNIVERSITY COLLEGE DUBLIN, EDINBURGH, IMPERIAL COLLEGE LONDON, KING'S COLLEGE LONDON, OXFORD, READING, SOUTHAMPTON, UNIVERSITY COLLEGE LONDON, WARWICK
Please check with your university careers service for full details of local events.

MINIMUM ENTRY REQUIREMENTS
2.1 Degree

APPLICATION DEADLINE
Year-round recruitment
Early application advised.

FURTHER INFORMATION
www.Top100GraduateEmployers.com
Register now for the latest news, campus events, work experience and graduate vacancies at **Huawei***.*

PASSION UNLOCKS POTENTIAL

#LifeatHuawei

Huawei is proud to offer inspiring, fast-moving careers for graduates at locations across the UK.

Our graduates get the opportunity to learn and develop in a cutting-edge international company, taking on stimulating roles that will kick-start incredible careers.

Find out more at **gradcracker.com/hub/739/huawei**

HUAWEI

twitter.com/IBMCareersUKI facebook.com/IBMCareersUKI

youtube.com/IBM linkedin.com/company/ibm

IBM is one of the world's largest technology and consulting firms. However, at IBM, work is more than a job - it's a calling: To build. To design. To code. To consult. To make markets. To invent. To collaborate. Not just to do something better, but to attempt things that people never thought possible.

IBM's graduate scheme will give graduates everything they need to build the kind of career they want. With graduate salaries starting at £30,000, a flexible benefits package and opportunities in consulting, technology and design, they will work on challenging projects, have real responsibility, and have access to world class opportunities. They'll be able to collaborate with people who are open-minded and excited about the same things they are.

IBM are looking for enthusiastic, driven and innovative individuals from any degree background. For the company's graduate schemes, applicants will have needed to achieve a 2:1 or higher in any degree discipline. IBM's most successful graduates share a distinct set of characteristics. These begin with energy and creativity, along with a clear focus on delivering exceptional customer service. IBM look for eight specific competencies during the application process: adaptability, communication, client focus, creative problem solving, teamwork, passion for IBM and taking ownership. If potential applicants love working with people and they thrive in a collaborative culture, then they'll fit right in.

Skills development is key to an IBMer's success. To further enhance their Professional Development, there are opportunities for coaching and mentoring, and these graduates will even get a dedicated manager. They will then have the opportunity to apply their knowledge in a commercial environment, via 'on-the-job training', adding value to IBM and its clients.

GRADUATE VACANCIES IN 2020

CONSULTING

TECHNOLOGY

NUMBER OF VACANCIES
150+ graduate jobs

LOCATIONS OF VACANCIES

STARTING SALARY FOR 2020
£30,000

UNIVERSITY VISITS IN 2019-20
ABERYSTWYTH, ASTON, BATH, BIRMINGHAM, BRADFORD, BRISTOL, BRUNEL, CARDIFF, DURHAM, EXETER, IMPERIAL COLLEGE LONDON, KING'S COLLEGE LONDON, LEEDS, LEICESTER, LIVERPOOL, LOUGHBOROUGH, MANCHESTER, NOTTINGHAM, NOTTINGHAM TRENT, OXFORD, OXFORD BROOKES, READING, SOUTHAMPTON, UNIVERSITY COLLEGE LONDON, WARWICK
Please check with your university careers service for full details of local events.

MINIMUM ENTRY REQUIREMENTS
2.1 Degree

APPLICATION DEADLINE
Varies by function

FURTHER INFORMATION
www.Top100GraduateEmployers.com
Register now for the latest news, campus events, work experience and graduate vacancies at IBM.

Let's put smart to work.™

Do your best work ever.

What can you do at IBM?

Our Graduate schemes will give you everything you need to build the career you want. You will work on challenging projects, have real responsibility and have access to world class opportunities. With the support of 380,000 collegues worldwide, you'll gain the experience, skills and contacts you need to help us solve some of our client's toughest challenges.

ibm.com/jobs/uk

Bianca
Joined 2008

f IBMCareersUKI

y IBMCareersUKI

(IM) irwinmitchell
solicitors

irwinmitchell.com/graduates

twitter.com/IMgraduates 🐦   earlycareers@irwinmitchell.com ✉

Irwin Mitchell are proud to be the UK's largest full service law firm. Founded in 1912, there is a strong national presence covering corporate law, personal injury and private wealth. The 'expert hand, human touch' philosophy resonates throughout the firm and its 3,000 employees.

The national firm offers training contracts at 11 different offices across the UK. Trainees choose between either Business Legal Services (BLS) or Personal Legal Services (PLS). Within BLS, seat rotations include areas such as banking and finance, insolvency, litigation and employment. PLS offers both personal injury seats including serious injury and medical negligence, but also private wealth seats such as wills, trust and estate disputes, court of protection and family law.

Trainees will complete four training seats over two years, interacting with partners and senior associates. This gives them the opportunity to gain a diverse set of experiences, whilst learning and working with some of the most highly regarded legal minds. At Irwin Mitchell, the trainees need to be passionate about the firm, client focused, display emotional intelligence, and possess strong analytical and problem solving skills.

A large number of training contracts are offered to those who have previously completed a legal work placement with the firm; therefore it is recommended to apply to the scheme where possible. This gives candidates an insight into the firm, the type of work trainees carry out and the people they will work with. There is a strong emphasis on well-being, smart working and a range of benefits to support the trainee's career at the firm.

Irwin Mitchell welcomes candidates from all backgrounds and offers real responsibility, supportive supervision and close client contact. The awards they have won show their commitment to clients and employees alike.

GRADUATE VACANCIES IN 2020
LAW

NUMBER OF VACANCIES
50 graduate jobs
For training contracts starting in 2022.

LOCATIONS OF VACANCIES

STARTING SALARY FOR 2020
£26,500-£38,000

UNIVERSITY VISITS IN 2019-20
BIRMINGHAM, BRISTOL, CAMBRIDGE, DURHAM, EXETER, KENT, LEEDS, LIVERPOOL, MANCHESTER, NEWCASTLE, NORTHUMBRIA, NOTTINGHAM, SHEFFIELD, SOUTHAMPTON, SUSSEX, WARWICK, YORK
Please check with your university careers service for full details of local events.

APPLICATION DEADLINE
12th January 2020

FURTHER INFORMATION
www.Top100GraduateEmployers.com
Register now for the latest news, campus events, work experience and graduate vacancies at Irwin Mitchell.

GRADUATE VACANCIES IN 2020

ENGINEERING

LOGISTICS

RESEARCH & DEVELOPMENT

TECHNOLOGY

NUMBER OF VACANCIES
150-200 graduate jobs

LOCATIONS OF VACANCIES

A tech-driven revolution is transforming the industry, and Jaguar Land Rover are on a journey to lead that transformation: a journey that requires people who can see the opportunity in a challenge. So, finding the next generation of innovators – bright and passionate people – is crucial.

Jaguar Land Rover is a British technology company with a global reach. They are harnessing technology to make driving smarter, safer and cleaner. Graduates can help create a world in which responsible, sustainable vehicles revolutionise the driving experience for generations.

New recruits need a creative and commercially focused approach to their work. Bring that, and Jaguar Land Rover has all the opportunities and rewards to help graduates learn, develop and apply their skills. The graduate scheme has been designed to be as inspiring as the vehicles that successful applicants will help to design, engineer and sell. As one of the UK's largest investors in research and innovation, education is a critical part of Jaguar Land Rover's business strategy and ambition. It aims to hire the best talent and, then, through lifelong education and training programmes, to help those people fulfill their potential. These opportunities lie right across the business, from engineering, manufacturing and software design to commercial and business areas.

As would be expected from two of the world's most revered brands, a range of rewards and benefits await those who have the initiative, vision and drive to contribute to the organisation's global success – including a competitive salary, joining bonus, pension scheme and discount car purchase scheme. There is also the opportunity to study for a chartered qualification as part of the programme.

All this, and more, makes Jaguar Land Rover an enviable place for graduates to start their journey.

STARTING SALARY FOR 2020
£29,000
Plus a £2,000 joining bonus.

UNIVERSITY VISITS IN 2019-20
ASTON, BIRMINGHAM, BRISTOL, BRUNEL, CAMBRIDGE, TRINITY COLLEGE DUBLIN, UNIVERSITY COLLEGE DUBLIN, DURHAM, GLASGOW, IMPERIAL COLLEGE LONDON, LEICESTER, LIVERPOOL, LOUGHBOROUGH, MANCHESTER, NOTTINGHAM, OXFORD, SHEFFIELD, SOUTHAMPTON, STRATHCLYDE, WARWICK
Please check with your university careers service for full details of local events.

MINIMUM ENTRY REQUIREMENTS
2.2 Degree

FURTHER INFORMATION
www.Top100GraduateEmployers.com
Register now for the latest news, campus events, work experience and graduate vacancies at Jaguar Land Rover.

IMAGINE WHAT'S POSSIBLE.
SEE B⹃YOND

Embrace a future of brand new possibilities. Now's the time to be part of a truly transformational journey – both for our business and your career.

As we surge forwards with our plans for autonomous and connected vehicles, electrification and game-changing technology, we've opened up a world of new challenges, ideas and opportunities. If you want to have the chance to think beyond what's gone before and make a difference, this is it.

jaguarlandrovercareers.com

At Johnson & Johnson, good health forms the foundation of vibrant lives. For more than 130 years, the company has aimed to keep people well at all ages and at all stages of life. Today, as the world's largest and most broadly-based healthcare company, it is committed to using its reach and size for the good of humanity.

At J&J, there is a team of more than 130,000 employees working across 60 countries to change the trajectory of human health for all. That sentiment applies to the company's people too. J&J's goal for 2020 is to have the world's healthiest workforce, and it has many programmes in place to help achieve that. More than 90% of its employees around the world have access to programmes that support healthy living, such as energy management training, which integrates the sciences of performance, psychology, physiology and nutrition to help achieve sustained high performance.

J&J operates across Pharmaceuticals, Medical Devices and Consumer Products through more than 275 companies. Being part of such a diverse and growing global business opens up a range of opportunities. Graduate and placement roles span many areas, offering potential to work on dynamic and challenging projects that matter to people everywhere. As an employee, each graduate can also join programmes abroad and work in regions of their choice to further build skill sets, forge their own path and reinvent themselves. Whatever their background, gender, ethnicity or sexual orientation, there's a place for all graduates to join a brilliant mix of people and revolutionise healthcare.

By joining a company that has been carving out the future of healthcare for more than 130 years, employees are offered careers as limitless as the lives they touch. It's as simple as that. Start building a career with purpose at J&J and make the next generation the healthiest yet.

GRADUATE VACANCIES IN 2020

ENGINEERING
FINANCE
MARKETING
RESEARCH & DEVELOPMENT
SALES

NUMBER OF VACANCIES
25-30 graduate jobs

LOCATIONS OF VACANCIES

STARTING SALARY FOR 2020
£Competitive

UNIVERSITY VISITS IN 2019-20
Please check with your university careers service for full details of local events.

MINIMUM ENTRY REQUIREMENTS
2.1 Degree

APPLICATION DEADLINE
Varies by function

FURTHER INFORMATION
www.Top100GraduateEmployers.com
Register now for the latest news, campus events, work experience and graduate vacancies at Johnson & Johnson.

Your next breakthrough belongs at Johnson & Johnson. JOIN US.

A vaccine for HIV. AI that discovers life-saving drugs. Digital health tools to track symptoms and treatments. It's all happening at Johnson & Johnson.

Here, your impact is amplified and no one is smarter than everyone. At J&J, our power is in the collective, among 275+ companies focused on consumer products, pharmaceuticals, and medical devices. Whatever your role or career goals, we make sure that you have the support and tools you need to live your best life, however you define it.

With locations in 60+ countries, together with experienced colleagues and immense resources, you can change the trajectory of human health, one breakthrough at a time.

Working with us can change everything. Including YOU.

Johnson & Johnson

CAREERS.JNJ.COM

J.P. Morgan are committed to helping businesses and markets grow and develop in more than 100 countries. Over the last 200 years, they have evolved to meet the complex financial needs of some of the world's largest companies, as well as many of the smaller businesses driving industry change.

J.P. Morgan work hard to do the right thing for their clients, shareholders and the firm every day. Joining the firm means learning from experts in a collaborative team environment where successful applicants will be supported to make an immediate impact from the start.

They want to see applicants' creativity, communications skills and drive. Whilst academic achievements are important, they're also looking for individuality and passion, as demonstrated by extra-curricular activities. J.P. Morgan invest in helping graduates fulfil their potential as they build their career at the firm. Internship and graduate positions are available firmwide, so applicants are encouraged to learn as much as possible about the different business areas and roles. They also offer pre-internship programmes, such as Spring Week, which provide insight into the finance industry and their programmes. They often hire directly from these opportunities – giving successful applicants early exposure to the firm and how they do business. The internship and full-time programmes they hire into are: asset management, corporate analyst development, data science & machine learning, global finance & business management, human resources, investment banking, markets, quantitative research, risk, software engineer, tech connect, wealth management, wholesale payments and corporate banking.

Working with a team committed to doing their best, earning the trust of their clients, and encouraging employees to fulfil their potential – that's what it means to be part of J.P. Morgan.

GRADUATE VACANCIES IN 2020

ACCOUNTANCY

FINANCE

GENERAL MANAGEMENT

HUMAN RESOURCES

INVESTMENT BANKING

TECHNOLOGY

NUMBER OF VACANCIES
500+ graduate jobs

LOCATIONS OF VACANCIES

Vacancies also available in Europe, the USA, Asia and elsewhere in the world.

STARTING SALARY FOR 2020
£Competitive

UNIVERSITY VISITS IN 2019-20
Please check with your university careers service for full details of local events.

APPLICATION DEADLINE
24th November 2019

FURTHER INFORMATION
www.Top100GraduateEmployers.com
Register now for the latest news, campus events, work experience and graduate vacancies at J.P. Morgan.

J.P.Morgan

All minds wanted. Especially yours.

Our programs are now open, apply by 24 November

We're looking for students from all majors and backgrounds to join our diverse, global team.

As a top employer in financial services, J.P. Morgan does much more than manage money. We create unexpected solutions to help individuals, companies, institutions and governments tackle financial and business challenges. That's why we need diverse minds like yours.

Here, you'll have more chances to continuously innovate, learn and make a positive impact for our clients, customers and communities. We offer internships in over 12 different business areas with 3 Early Insight Programs to introduce you to the industry and our company.

To see how you can join our collaborative team, visit **jpmorgan.com/careers** to learn more about our programs and upcoming on-campus and virtual events.

We look forward to meeting you.

kpmgcareers.co.uk

GRADUATE VACANCIES IN 2020

ACCOUNTANCY
CONSULTING
FINANCE
GENERAL MANAGEMENT
HUMAN RESOURCES
TECHNOLOGY

NUMBER OF VACANCIES
Around 1,200 graduate jobs

LOCATIONS OF VACANCIES

KPMG in the UK is part of a global network of firms. Its largest practice is Audit, which provides independent challenge and delivers quality audits to a range of companies. In Tax & Pensions, Consulting, Deal Advisory and Technology & Engineering, KPMG helps clients to solve complex business challenges.

From joining, graduate and undergraduate trainees at the firm will undertake intellectually-stimulating challenges alongside some of the brightest minds in business. Trainees will gain exposure to a range of sectors and companies, from the biggest multinationals through to the most innovative start-ups.

KPMG colleagues come from all sorts of degree disciplines and backgrounds, bringing diverse perspectives, but sharing a natural curiosity and a desire to work together and explore new ideas, inspire change and deliver exceptional results.

Technology & Engineering is a rapidly growing part of the firm and is fundamental to everything KPMG does. Trainees will have access to advanced technologies, such as artificial intelligence and the latest Cloud tools. KPMG tools – such as KPMG Clara, the firm's progressive global collaboration and analytics tool – enable their audit teams to provide quality insights and consistency across all audit engagements.

KPMG has a simple vision: to be the clear choice for its clients, its people and the communities it works in. All graduates will benefit from funded, relevant professional qualifications or accreditations, and the support they need to build a rewarding career. With volunteering days and numerous community initiatives, trainees are encouraged to make a difference beyond the office, too.

Life at KPMG means being part of a fast-moving, intellectually challenging and supportive community, where graduates and undergraduates are inspired to learn, grow and thrive.

STARTING SALARY FOR 2020
£Competitive
Plus a great range of benefits –
see website for details.

UNIVERSITY VISITS IN 2019-20
ABERDEEN, ASTON, BIRMINGHAM, BRISTOL, CAMBRIDGE, CARDIFF, CITY, EXETER, GLASGOW, HERIOT-WATT, IMPERIAL COLLEGE LONDON, KING'S COLLEGE LONDON, LANCASTER, LEEDS, LEICESTER, LIVERPOOL, LONDON SCHOOL OF ECONOMICS, MANCHESTER, NEWCASTLE, NOTTINGHAM TRENT, OXFORD, PLYMOUTH, QUEEN MARY LONDON, READING, ROYAL HOLLOWAY, SHEFFIELD, SOUTHAMPTON, STRATHCLYDE, SURREY, UNIVERSITY COLLEGE LONDON, WARWICK
Please check with your university careers
service for full details of local events.

MINIMUM ENTRY REQUIREMENTS
2.1 Degree
Degree in any discipline.
120 UCAS points
300 UCAS points for those who passed
exams before 2017.
Please see website for details.

APPLICATION DEADLINE
Year-round recruitment
Early application advised.

FURTHER INFORMATION
www.Top100GraduateEmployers.com
Register now for the latest news, campus
events, work experience and graduate
vacancies at KPMG.

Let your curiosity lead you.

Graduate and undergraduate opportunities

At KPMG, curiosity could take you on a rewarding journey. We work side-by-side with clients to help them to solve some of their most complex business challenges, seeking the facts, applying insights and delivering quality results.

On our programmes, you'll have the opportunity to work with a variety of organisations, from the biggest multinationals through to the most innovative start-ups. You'll use your natural curiosity and fresh perspective to empower change and help businesses succeed now, and in the future. In return, we'll give you all the support you need to learn and grow. Join us in Audit, Tax & Pensions, Consulting, Deal Advisory, Technology & Engineering or KPMG Business Services and discover a career path full of rewards.

kpmgcareers.co.uk

Anticipate tomorrow. Deliver today.

L'ORÉAL

L'Oréal is the world's number one beauty company, with a portfolio of 36 international brands including L'Oréal Paris, Garnier and Lancôme, to name a few. L'Oréal's ambition is to become the world's leading beauty tech company, through digital innovation, product design and world-class consumer journeys.

L'Oréal UK and Ireland, the local subsidiary and leading player in the multi-billion pound beauty industry in the UK, look for an entrepreneurial mind-set in their graduates. They also believe in developing their people from the ground up, providing their employees with the opportunity to grow within the company and build a career with them. As a result, a portion of management trainee roles are filled by individuals from their internship and spring insight programmes, creating a well-rounded junior talent journey at L'Oréal. The remainder of the graduate roles are sourced from the external market, to ensure an equal opportunity for all potential candidates to join this exciting business.

On the Management Trainee Programme, graduates work in functions across the business, gaining a sense of life at L'Oréal. With three different rotations in their chosen stream, graduates are free to develop their talent and discover new possibilities, shaping their future careers as they go. With on-the-job training and their own HR Sponsor, graduates will progress into operational roles in as little as 18 months.

L'Oréal UKI is committed to being one of the top employers in the UK, fostering a workplace where everyone feels welcome and valued. Promoting gender equality, driving diversity and inclusion, addressing mental health and establishing evolving workplace practices are a key focus. Through 'Sharing Beauty with All', L'Oréal's global sustainability programme, the business is driving change across all areas including product design, packaging, supply chain and consumer behaviour.

GRADUATE VACANCIES IN 2020
GENERAL MANAGEMENT
MARKETING
SALES

NUMBER OF VACANCIES
28 graduate jobs

LOCATIONS OF VACANCIES

STARTING SALARY FOR 2020
£30,000

UNIVERSITY VISITS IN 2019-20
BATH, UNIVERSITY COLLEGE DUBLIN, DURHAM, EDINBURGH, EXETER, KING'S COLLEGE LONDON, LANCASTER, LEEDS, LEICESTER, LIVERPOOL, LONDON SCHOOL OF ECONOMICS, LOUGHBOROUGH, MANCHESTER, NEWCASTLE, NOTTINGHAM, NOTTINGHAM TRENT, OXFORD, OXFORD BROOKES, READING, SHEFFIELD, ST ANDREWS, UNIVERSITY COLLEGE LONDON, WARWICK, YORK
Please check with your university careers service for full details of local events.

APPLICATION DEADLINE
Year-round recruitment
Early application advised.

FURTHER INFORMATION
www.Top100GraduateEmployers.com
Register now for the latest news, campus events, work experience and graduate vacancies at L'Oréal.

Lidl are proud pioneers in the world of retail. With over 760 stores, 13 warehouses and 22,500 employees in the UK alone, they're undoubtedly one of the fastest growing retailers in the country. With their ambitious expansion plans for UK growth over the coming years, it's clear they don't like to stand still.

Continually challenging and changing the world of grocery retail, Lidl want to make their stores, products and shopping experience better than ever. Lidl is committed to driving various responsibility programmes, including charity partnerships, food redistribution, recycling schemes and sustainably sourcing for the future.

Lidl is a performance-driven business, and that's exactly what they are looking for in their graduates. They are not looking for one type of person. They are looking for ambitious, committed people with personality and potential. Potential to become one of Lidl's future leaders.

Lidl's structured graduate programmes across all areas of the business are designed to develop students and graduates quickly by challenging them to reach their potential. Experiences span Lidl's stores, warehouses and regional offices, giving graduates the best possible exposure to the business, along with a range of opportunities to develop their skills and leadership expertise. Throughout each individual role, graduates will gain soft skill & operational development through a carefully structured training plan, giving a clear development path. These graduates learn from the best managers and develop their operational and management abilities from day one – progression from there is down to the individual.

Lidl is an award-winning employer: graduates benefit from competitive salaries, fast-tracked development and stimulating work with world-class teams.

GRADUATE VACANCIES IN 2020
GENERAL MANAGEMENT
LOGISTICS
PURCHASING
RETAILING
SALES

NUMBER OF VACANCIES
60+ graduate jobs

LOCATIONS OF VACANCIES

STARTING SALARY FOR 2020
£37,000

UNIVERSITY VISITS IN 2019-20
ASTON, BATH, BIRMINGHAM, CARDIFF, EDINBURGH, ESSEX, EXETER, GLASGOW, KENT, LEEDS, LIVERPOOL, MANCHESTER, NEWCASTLE, NORTHUMBRIA, NOTTINGHAM, OXFORD, PLYMOUTH, ROYAL HOLLOWAY, STRATHCLYDE, SWANSEA, UNIVERSITY COLLEGE LONDON
Please check with your university careers service for full details of local events.

MINIMUM ENTRY REQUIREMENTS
2.2 Degree

APPLICATION DEADLINE
Late December 2019

FURTHER INFORMATION
www.Top100GraduateEmployers.com
Register now for the latest news, campus events, work experience and graduate vacancies at Lidl.

CHOOSE
YOUR
FUTURE.

Our rotational graduate programmes give huge variety, all-round experience and the skills to grow a career that's going places.

BRING YOUR BEST. WE'LL DO THE REST.

lidlgraduatecareers.co.uk

Linklaters

From a shifting geopolitical landscape to the exponential growth in FinTech, this is a time of unprecedented change. Linklaters is ready. They go further to support clients, with market-leading legal insight and innovation. And they go further for each other, too.

When people join Linklaters, they find colleagues they want to work with. Inspiring, personable professionals who are generous with their time and always happy to help. Because, to be best in class, Linklaters looks for open minded, team-spirited individuals who will collaborate – and innovate – to deliver the smartest solutions for clients. Linklaters recruits candidates from a range of different backgrounds and disciplines, not just law. Why? Because those candidates bring with them a set of unique skills and perspectives that can help to challenge conventional thinking and inspire different approaches to client problems.

All Linklaters trainees benefit from pioneering learning and development opportunities, and an inclusive working culture that encourages them to fulfil their potential. Non-law graduates can take a one-year conversion course, the Graduate Diploma in Law. And all graduates complete the bespoke, accelerated Legal Practice Course before starting training contracts.

Then, over two years, trainees take four six-month seats (placements) in different practice areas and sometimes abroad. They work on high-profile deals across a global network of 30 offices, and gain the knowledge they need to qualify. And throughout their career, they enjoy the advantage of world-class training, courtesy of the Linklaters Law & Business School.

With their uniquely future-focused culture and high-profile, global opportunities, Linklaters provides the ideal preparation for a rewarding career, no matter what the future holds. Great change is here. Get ready.

GRADUATE VACANCIES IN 2020
LAW

NUMBER OF VACANCIES
100 graduate jobs
For training contracts starting in 2022.

LOCATIONS OF VACANCIES

STARTING SALARY FOR 2020
£47,000

UNIVERSITY VISITS IN 2019-20
BELFAST, BIRMINGHAM, BRISTOL, CAMBRIDGE, CITY, TRINITY COLLEGE DUBLIN, UNIVERSITY COLLEGE DUBLIN, DURHAM, EDINBURGH, EXETER, KING'S COLLEGE LONDON, LEEDS, LEICESTER, LONDON SCHOOL OF ECONOMICS, MANCHESTER, NOTTINGHAM, NOTTINGHAM TRENT, OXFORD, OXFORD BROOKES, QUEEN MARY LONDON, SCHOOL OF AFRICAN STUDIES, SHEFFIELD, SOUTHAMPTON, ST ANDREWS, UNIVERSITY COLLEGE LONDON, WARWICK, YORK
Please check with your university careers service for full details of local events.

MINIMUM ENTRY REQUIREMENTS
2.1 Degree
Relevant degree required for some roles.

APPLICATION DEADLINE
Varies by function

FURTHER INFORMATION
www.Top100GraduateEmployers.com
*Register now for the latest news, campus events, work experience and graduate vacancies at **Linklaters**.*

Great change is here.

Linklaters

Are you ready?

From a shifting geopolitical landscape
to the exponential growth in FinTech,
this is a time of unprecedented change.

At Linklaters, we're ready. Our people
go further to support our clients,
with market-leading legal insight and
innovation. And we go further for each
other, too. We're people you want to work
with, generous with our time and ready
to help. So no matter what the future
holds, with us you'll be one step ahead.
Great change is here. Get ready.

Find out more at careers.linklaters.com

LLOYDS
BANKING GROUP

lloydsbankinggrouptalent.com
facebook.com/discoverwhatmatters [f]   lloydsbankinggrouptalent@tmpw.co.uk ✉
instagram.com/LBGtalent [O]   twitter.com/LBGtalent [y]

GRADUATE VACANCIES IN 2020
- ACCOUNTANCY
- CONSULTING
- ENGINEERING
- FINANCE
- GENERAL MANAGEMENT
- INVESTMENT BANKING
- MARKETING
- SALES
- TECHNOLOGY

NUMBER OF VACANCIES
200+ graduate jobs

LOCATIONS OF VACANCIES

STARTING SALARY FOR 2020
£31,000
Plus a discretionary bonus and flexible working.

UNIVERSITY VISITS IN 2019-20
ASTON, BIRMINGHAM, BRISTOL, CAMBRIDGE, CARDIFF, DURHAM, EDINBURGH, EXETER, GLASGOW, IMPERIAL COLLEGE LONDON, KING'S COLLEGE LONDON, LEEDS, LIVERPOOL, LONDON SCHOOL OF ECONOMICS, MANCHESTER, NEWCASTLE, NOTTINGHAM, OXFORD, QUEEN MARY LONDON, STRATHCLYDE, UNIVERSITY COLLEGE LONDON, WARWICK, YORK
Please check with your university careers service for full details of local events.

MINIMUM ENTRY REQUIREMENTS
2.2 Degree

APPLICATION DEADLINE
Varies by function

FURTHER INFORMATION
www.Top100GraduateEmployers.com
Register now for the latest news, campus events, work experience and graduate vacancies at Lloyds Banking Group.

As the UK's largest retail and digital bank, Lloyds Banking Group is helping redefine financial services by using the latest technology to support over 26 million customers through their main brands like Lloyds Bank, Halifax, Scottish Widows and Bank of Scotland.

As Lloyds Banking Group works to redefine financial services for the digital age, there is a need for a broader range of skills and experience, which means graduates don't necessarily need a business or finance degree to embark on a career in banking.

Instead, Lloyds Banking Group is looking for passionate, inquisitive individuals who can bring their unique perspective to work and help drive the business forward. Whether it's building relationships with global clients or developing the next generation of technology, graduates will be building the bank of the future from day one.

In return, graduates will enjoy a range of opportunities that may include learning how to lead, coding next generation banking products, or shaping business strategy. There are a variety of graduate programmes and internship opportunities to choose from, ranging from commercial banking and finance to data science and enterprise leadership. Graduates will receive all the training and development, support and mentoring they'll need to learn about the industry and develop important strengths and capabilities. On top of this, Lloyds Banking Group offers a fantastic range of benefits including professional qualifications.

Lloyds Banking Group provides the perfect opportunity for a graduate to start their career at an organisation with the reach and scale to make a real impact for customers, businesses and communities across the UK.

WHAT IMPACT WILL YOU MAKE?

We look beyond areas of study because we know that diverse skillsets are essential to great work. Daniel's LBG journey started with an internship and he now develops technology that transforms people's lives. Start your journey here – and join us in helping Britain prosper.

Discover careers with real impact at
lloydsbankinggrouptalent.com

MARS

GRADUATE VACANCIES IN 2020

ENGINEERING
FINANCE
GENERAL MANAGEMENT
HUMAN RESOURCES
MARKETING
PURCHASING
RESEARCH & DEVELOPMENT
SALES

NUMBER OF VACANCIES
25-30 graduate jobs

LOCATIONS OF VACANCIES

Vacancies also available in Europe, Asia, and elsewhere in the world.

STARTING SALARY FOR 2020
£32,000
Plus a £2,000 joining bonus.

UNIVERSITY VISITS IN 2019-20
BATH, BIRMINGHAM, CAMBRIDGE,
DURHAM, EXETER, LEEDS, NOTTINGHAM,
OXFORD, WARWICK
Please check with your university careers service for full details of local events.

MINIMUM ENTRY REQUIREMENTS
2.1 Degree

APPLICATION DEADLINE
6th December 2019

FURTHER INFORMATION
www.Top100GraduateEmployers.com
Register now for the latest news, campus events, work experience and graduate vacancies at Mars.

Think Maltesers®, M&Ms®, Uncle Ben's®, Pedigree®, Whiskas®, Extra® and Orbit®, some of the nation's best-loved and well-known brands. Think the world's third-largest food company, with 115,000 associates and international operations across the world. Know what makes Mars special? Think again.

Sure, Mars is one of the world's leading food companies, but it's more like a community than a corporate – because it's still a private, family-owned business built up of a Mars family of associates. Associates at Mars are united and guided by The Five Principles – Quality, Responsibility, Mutuality, Efficiency and Freedom. These are key to the culture and help associates to make business decisions they are proud of.

The culture at Mars is relationship-driven – and it's how these relationships are built that's most important. Collaborating with others is key to getting things done. Mars encourages open communication as this builds relationships of trust and respect.

Mars want to stretch and challenge associates every day to help them reach their full potential. So they take learning and development seriously – it makes good business sense for Mars to have people performing at the top of their game. With great managers, mentors, coaches and peers, graduates will be supported the whole way. And they will support other associates on their journey too.

At Mars, graduates are offered an unrivalled opportunity to make a difference in their roles from day one. Mars wants everything they do to matter – from the smallest thing to the biggest – and Mars wants their work to make a positive difference to customers, suppliers, associates and the world as a whole. Graduates will have endless support to develop both personally and professionally, creating a start to an exciting and fulfilling career.

Make reading this the start of your career.

Ready for a Mars Leadership Experience?

The future you want tomorrow starts with the decision you make today. Each of our 110,000 Associates were once where you are now, deciding if Mars is the right place to build a future. If you're ready to manage projects, build trust, take on real roles with local and international exposure, then one of our Mars Leadership Experiences could be exactly what you've been looking for. So, get ready to collaborate, seize a great development opportunity and make a difference – today and every day.

Make today count, visit
Mars.co.uk/graduates

#TomorrowStartsToday

MARS

GRADUATE VACANCIES IN 2020
GENERAL MANAGEMENT

NUMBER OF VACANCIES
30 graduate jobs

LOCATIONS OF VACANCIES

McDonald's is the biggest family restaurant business in the world and has been a part of the UK for 45 years. It has nearly 1,350 restaurants employing over 129,000 people who work together to deliver great tasting food with service that their customers know and trust.

Training and developing people has been at the heart of the McDonald's business throughout its 45 years in the UK. Each year the company invests over £43 million in developing its people and providing opportunities for progression.

Attracting, retaining and engaging the best people is key to their business. They have a proven track record of career progression, and prospective managers can create a long-term career with one of the world's most recognised and successful brands.

A graduate job at McDonald's is focused on restaurant management – it involves overseeing the performance and development of an average of 80 employees and identifying ways in which to improve customer service, build sales and profitability.

Following the training period, which can last up to six months, Trainee Managers are promoted to Assistant Managers and become part of the core restaurant management team. Successful Trainee Managers can progress to managing all aspects of a multi-million pound business – opportunities can then arise to progress to area management roles or secondments in support departments. Trainee Managers need to be logical thinkers, have a great attitude and be committed to delivering a great customer experience.

Working for a progressive company has its perks – including a host of benefits such as a quarterly bonus scheme, six weeks of holiday allowance, meal allowance, private healthcare and access to discounts at hundreds of retailers.

STARTING SALARY FOR 2020
£22,000

UNIVERSITY VISITS IN 2019-20
Please check with your university careers service for full details of local events.

APPLICATION DEADLINE
Year-round recruitment

FURTHER INFORMATION
www.Top100GraduateEmployers.com
Register now for the latest news, campus events, work experience and graduate vacancies at **McDonald's**.

Setting myself up for the future

With McDonald's, I can...

Our Trainee Manager Programme is the first step to managing a £multi-million restaurant employing over 80 staff.

After six months of training and learning the basics, our Trainee Managers are promoted to Assistant Managers- but if you've got the drive and ambition, there's no limit to how far you can go.

To find out more about working and learning with us visit

people.mcdonalds.co.uk

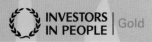

SECURITYSERVICE MI5

GRADUATE VACANCIES IN 2020
GENERAL MANAGEMENT
INTELLIGENCE GATHERING
TECHNOLOGY

NUMBER OF VACANCIES
200+ graduate jobs

LOCATIONS OF VACANCIES

MI5 helps safeguard the UK against threats to national security including terrorism and espionage. It investigates suspect individuals and organisations to gather intelligence relating to security threats. MI5 also advises the critical national infrastructure on protective security measures.

Graduates from a range of backgrounds join MI5 for stimulating and rewarding careers, in a supportive environment, whilst enjoying a good work-life balance. Many graduates join the Intelligence Officer Development Programme, which is a structured four year programme designed to teach new joiners about MI5 investigations and give them the skills to run them. After completing one post of two years, or two posts of one year, in areas which teach aspects of intelligence work, and subject to successful completion of a final assessment, graduates will then take up an investigative post as a fully trained Intelligence Officer.

MI5 also deals with vast amounts of data, and interpreting that data is vital to its intelligence work. The Intelligence and Data Analyst Development Programme is a structured five-year programme which prepares individuals with potential to be part of this specialist career stream. It will take them from the basics through to the most innovative data analytical techniques. As they progress, they will use their analytical expertise in different teams across a range of MI5 investigations.

MI5 also offers a structured Technology Graduate Development Programme, which gives graduates the experience, knowledge and skills they need to be an effective technology professional in the organisation's pioneering IT function.

Graduates who are looking for a rewarding career in corporate services can join MI5 as Business Enablers, where they can develop a breadth of experience undertaking corporate roles across a range of business areas, before having the opportunity to specialise in a particular area.

STARTING SALARY FOR 2020
£31,000+

UNIVERSITY VISITS IN 2019-20
Please check with your university careers service for full details of local events.

MINIMUM ENTRY REQUIREMENTS
2.2 Degree

APPLICATION DEADLINE
Varies by function

FURTHER INFORMATION
www.Top100GraduateEmployers.com
Register now for the latest news, campus events, work experience and graduate vacancies at MI5.

YOUR
POTENTIAL IS
GREATER THAN
FICTION

Intelligence Officer
Development Programme

**£31,807, rising to £34,385
after one year**

You might think that working for MI5 as an Intelligence Officer is the stuff of imagination. But it's a real job for real people. In fact, we need individuals from a diverse range of backgrounds to bring different perspectives and experiences to the role.

You might assume that you don't have what it takes but you could well have the attributes we're looking for. We need people with excellent communication skills, who enjoy problem solving and have the ability to see the bigger picture. We'll teach you the rest through a structured development programme where you'll learn how to help keep the country safe. And while you might think it's a stressful, intense job, it's actually all about team-work and the environment is incredibly supportive. You also can't take your work home with you, so that's the work-life balance sorted!

MI5 is committed to equal opportunities and to reflecting the society we protect. All applications are welcome, but we particularly welcome applications from women and Black, Asian and Minority Ethnic candidates.

To enjoy one of the most rewarding careers you can imagine, find out more about the Intelligence Officer Development Programme at **www.mi5.gov.uk/careers**

SECURITY SERVICE
MI5

Morgan Stanley

facebook.com/MorganStanley **f**   graduaterecruitmenteurope@morganstanley.com ✉
linkedin.com/company/morgan-stanley **in**   twitter.com/MorganStanley 𝕐
instagram.com/Morgan.Stanley 𝕆   youtube.com/MgStnly ▶

Morgan Stanley is one of the world's leading financial services firms. They generate, manage and distribute capital, helping businesses get the funds they need to develop innovative products and services that benefit millions. Their work is defined by the passion and dedication of their people, and their goals are achieved through hiring, training and rewarding the best possible talent.

At Morgan Stanley attitude is just as important as aptitude, and they want to work with and develop students and graduates who show integrity and commitment to their core values, who share their commitment to providing first-class client service, and who embrace change and innovation. Because the firm values a diversity of perspectives, it encourages people to be themselves and pursue their own interests.

There are numerous opportunities to learn, grow professionally and help put the power of capital to work. All of Morgan Stanley's programmes are designed to provide the knowledge and toolkit graduates need to develop quickly into an effective and successful professional in their chosen area. Training is not limited to the first weeks or months on the job, but continues throughout a graduate's career. Over time, they could become part of the next generation of leaders, and play a part in technological, scientific and cultural advancements that change the world forever.

Morgan Stanley believes that capital can work to benefit all. This success needs financial capital, but its foundation is intellectual capital. The talents and points of view of the diverse individuals working for them help to build their legacy and shape their future. This is why Morgan Stanley accepts applicants from all degree disciplines who demonstrate academic excellence.

GRADUATE VACANCIES IN 2020
FINANCE
HUMAN RESOURCES
INVESTMENT BANKING
TECHNOLOGY

NUMBER OF VACANCIES
200+ graduate jobs

LOCATIONS OF VACANCIES

STARTING SALARY FOR 2020
£Competitive

UNIVERSITY VISITS IN 2019-20
Please check with your university careers service for full details of local events.

MINIMUM ENTRY REQUIREMENTS
Strong academic background, 2.1 or equivalent preferred.

APPLICATION DEADLINE
Varies by function

FURTHER INFORMATION
www.Top100GraduateEmployers.com
*Register now for the latest news, campus events, work experience and graduate vacancies at **Morgan Stanley**.*

GRADUATE VACANCIES IN 2020

CONSULTING

ENGINEERING

TECHNOLOGY

NUMBER OF VACANCIES

280 graduate jobs

LOCATIONS OF VACANCIES

Mott MacDonald is a global engineering, management and development consultancy focused on guiding clients through many of the planet's most intricate challenges. By challenging norms and unlocking creativity, Mott MacDonald delivers long-lasting value for societies around the globe.

Improvement is at the heart of what Mott MacDonald offers. Better economic development, better social and environmental outcomes, better businesses and a better return on investment. Their 16,000-strong network of experts are joined-up across sectors and geographies, giving their graduates access to an exceptional breadth and depth of expertise and experience, enhancing their knowledge with the right support and guidance every step of the way.

The consultancy's employees, active in 150 countries, take leading roles on some of the world's highest profile projects, turning obstacles into elegant, sustainable solutions. Individuals who get satisfaction from working on projects that benefit communities around the world will thrive at Mott MacDonald. Additionally, as Mott MacDonald is an employee-owned company, it allows them to choose the work they take on and focus on the issues that are important.

Mott MacDonald's graduate schemes are more than just a standard graduate job. With the help of a dedicated learning and development team, the accredited schemes aim to give graduates the opportunity to continually progress and develop in their chosen field. The schemes have been created specifically to enable graduates to be the best that they can be. All entry-level professionals are enrolled into the Mott MacDonald graduate programme, a structured development programme introducing key business and commercial competencies.

STARTING SALARY FOR 2020

£28,000-£31,000

UNIVERSITY VISITS IN 2019-20

BATH, BIRMINGHAM, BRISTOL, CAMBRIDGE, CARDIFF, EDINBURGH, GLASGOW, HERIOT-WATT, IMPERIAL COLLEGE LONDON, LEEDS, MANCHESTER, NEWCASTLE, PLYMOUTH, READING, SHEFFIELD, STRATHCLYDE, SURREY, UNIVERSITY COLLEGE LONDON, WARWICK

Please check with your university careers service for full details of local events.

MINIMUM ENTRY REQUIREMENTS

2.1 Degree

APPLICATION DEADLINE

10th November 2019

FURTHER INFORMATION

www.Top100GraduateEmployers.com

Register now for the latest news, campus events, work experience and graduate vacancies at Mott MacDonald.

Unlocking creativity

Be part of a dedicated team delivering longlasting value at every stage of a project. Working in all areas of infrastructure, management and development, we look at challenges from a fresh angle, creating solutions that improve people's lives.

Opening opportunities with connected thinking.

mottmac.com/careers/graduate

networkrail.co.uk/careers/graduates

facebook.com/NetworkRailCareers **f**   GraduateCareers@networkrail.co.uk ✉

linkedin.com/company/network-rail **in**   twitter.com/NetworkRailJobs ▼

instagram.com/NetworkRail 📷   youtube.com/NetworkRail ▶

Network Rail own and operate the railway infrastructure in England, Scotland and Wales. Their purpose is to create a better railway for a better Britain. It is the fastest growing and safest rail network in Europe, presenting an abundance of opportunities for ambitious and enthusiastic graduates.

Network Rail have £47bn earmarked to invest in landmark projects and initiatives as part of their Railway Upgrade Plan. They are already making history through some of the largest engineering projects in Europe: Crossrail, Birmingham New Street Station, London Bridge, HS2 and Thameslink.

Although rail is a huge part of their business, they are also one of the largest land and property owners in Britain. They manage a portfolio that includes 18 of the biggest stations in Britain, the retail outlets inside them and the small businesses that live under their arches.

Network Rail are looking to invest in graduates who are committed to making a difference, to help transform Britain's rail infrastructure, transport network and economy for the 22nd century.

They have supported thousands of graduates through their diverse and challenging programmes. Graduates will have access to Westwood, their state-of-the-art training centre in Coventry, and six other training facilities.

There are two entry routes for graduates. Within Engineering there are three specific schemes: civil, electrical & electronic, and mechanical engineering.

In Business Management, applicants can choose from the following schemes: finance, general management, health, safety and environment, HR, IT & business services, project management, property and quantity surveying.

There are also summer and year in industry placements available for those who would like to find out what it is like to work for Network Rail before graduation.

GRADUATE VACANCIES IN 2020

ENGINEERING
FINANCE
GENERAL MANAGEMENT
HUMAN RESOURCES
PROPERTY
TECHNOLOGY

NUMBER OF VACANCIES
250 graduate jobs

LOCATIONS OF VACANCIES

STARTING SALARY FOR 2020
£26,500
Plus a £2,000 bonus and a 75% discount on season tickets (up to a maximum of £3,000).

UNIVERSITY VISITS IN 2019-20
BIRMINGHAM, BRUNEL, CAMBRIDGE, CARDIFF, EDINBURGH, GLASGOW, LOUGHBOROUGH, MANCHESTER, NEWCASTLE, NOTTINGHAM, QUEEN MARY LONDON, READING, SHEFFIELD, STRATHCLYDE, UNIVERSITY COLLEGE LONDON, WARWICK, YORK
Please check with your university careers service for full details of local events.

MINIMUM ENTRY REQUIREMENTS
2.2 Degree

APPLICATION DEADLINE
December 2019

FURTHER INFORMATION
www.Top100GraduateEmployers.com
Register now for the latest news, campus events, work experience and graduate vacancies at Network Rail.

The difference is you

Standout graduate and placement opportunities at Network Rail

 + +

We're investing £47bn to create a world-class railway that will really make a difference to rail travel in Britain.

We need you to help turn our plans into reality.

— **Are you ready for a career as bright and unique as you are?**

Opportunities available in:

Engineering
– Civil engineering
– Electrical & electronic engineering
– Mechanical engineering

Business management
– Finance
– General management
– Health, safety & environment
– Human resources
– IT & business services
– Project management
– Property
– Quantity Surveying

Find out more at
networkrail.co.uk/graduates

Newton isn't like most consultancies. At Newton, consultants are called in to crack some of the toughest challenges that businesses and public sector organisations face. They hire people with spirit, personality and bravery - and go to extraordinary lengths to build their skills and belief.

Newton trust the ingenuity of their people so deeply that they put their fee at risk to guarantee results for clients. And they believe in the impact of the solutions they create so much that they promise to stay on in each clients' businesses to make sure they get the results they need.

The business model is bold and disruptive – and it doesn't make things easy for consultants on the ground. But it does make things interesting. They regularly encounter problems and complexities that haven't been tackled before, and they don't have pre-fabricated answers to fall back on. They have to rely not just on their combined knowledge, but on their own courage, passion and self-belief.

They've already achieved amazing things as a team. For one retail client, they grew top line sales by £¼ bn and took 80,000 people through a change programme. On a major UK defence build programme, they saw a 64% improvement in cost performance. And elsewhere they've reduced Child in Need and Child Protection caseload numbers by 29%.

Newton are looking for extraordinary people to join as Operations Consultants and Digital Solutions Consultants. All consultants work alongside a variety of clients to design and implement programmes that deliver sustainable change working from the shop floor to the boardroom. They're encouraged to "get stuck right in" and use their initiative and creativity to deliver far-reaching and measurable results for clients, demanding better for them. Newton is an employer where, if graduates don't limit themselves, nothing will limit them.

GRADUATE VACANCIES IN 2020
CONSULTING

NUMBER OF VACANCIES
100 graduate jobs

LOCATIONS OF VACANCIES

STARTING SALARY FOR 2020
£45,000-£50,000 package
*Including a £5,000 car allowance.
Plus a sign-on bonus.*

UNIVERSITY VISITS IN 2019-20
BATH, BIRMINGHAM, BRISTOL, CAMBRIDGE, DURHAM, EDINBURGH, EXETER, IMPERIAL COLLEGE LONDON, LEEDS, LONDON SCHOOL OF ECONOMICS, MANCHESTER, OXFORD, ST ANDREWS, STRATHCLYDE, UNIVERSITY COLLEGE LONDON, WARWICK
Please check with your university careers service for full details of local events.

APPLICATION DEADLINE
25th December 2019

FURTHER INFORMATION
www.Top100GraduateEmployers.com
Register now for the latest news, campus events, work experience and graduate vacancies at Newton.

NEWTON

NEVER NOT HOME
BY SIX ON FRIDAY.
NEVER NOT NEWTON.

It's not just our focus on real-world results that sets Newton apart from other consulting firms. The way we look after our people is pretty out-of-the-ordinary too. For example, wherever you are in the country, whatever project you're working on, and whoever that project is with, your weekends will always be your own.

Find out more at **WorkAtNewton.com**

NATIONAL GRADUATE
DEVELOPMENT PROGRAMME
ngdp
FOR LOCAL GOVERNMENT

local.gov.uk/ngdp

twitter.com/ngdp_LGA 🐦   ngdp.support@local.gov.uk ✉

GRADUATE VACANCIES IN 2020

ACCOUNTANCY
FINANCE
GENERAL MANAGEMENT
HUMAN RESOURCES
LAW
MARKETING
MEDIA
PROPERTY
PURCHASING
RESEARCH & DEVELOPMENT
TECHNOLOGY

NUMBER OF VACANCIES
140 graduate jobs

LOCATIONS OF VACANCIES

STARTING SALARY FOR 2020
£25,295
Plus London weighting where appropriate.

The ngdp is a two-year graduate development programme which gives committed graduates the opportunity and training to fast-track their career in local government. Run by the Local Government Association, the ngdp is looking to equip the sector's next generation of high-calibre managers.

Local government is responsible for a range of vital services for people and businesses. They are a diverse and large employer, with more than one million people working in local government, providing more than 800 services to local communities. More than 1,200 graduates have completed the ngdp since 1999 and gained access to rewarding careers in and beyond the sector, with many currently holding influential managerial and policy roles.

The ngdp graduates are positioned to make a real contribution to shaping and implementing new ideas and initiatives in local government. Graduate trainees are employed by a participating council (or group of councils) for a minimum of two years, during which time they rotate between a series of placements in key areas of the council. Trainees can experience a range of roles in strategy, front-line service and support, to expand their perspective of local government's many different capacities and gain a flexible, transferrable skill set.

Ngdp graduates also benefit from being part of a national cohort of like-minded peers. Together they will participate in a national induction event, join an established knowledge-sharing network and gain a post-graduate qualification in Leadership and Management. The learning and development programme gives graduates the chance to learn from established professionals and also each other. The ngdp has been enabling graduates to build varied and rewarding careers for almost twenty years. Join now to start working in an exciting period of opportunity and change for the benefit of local communities.

UNIVERSITY VISITS IN 2019-20
BIRMINGHAM, BRISTOL, CARDIFF, DURHAM, EXETER, KEELE, KING'S COLLEGE LONDON, LANCASTER, LEEDS, LEICESTER, LIVERPOOL, LONDON SCHOOL OF ECONOMICS, NEWCASTLE, NORTHUMBRIA, NOTTINGHAM TRENT, OXFORD, PLYMOUTH, YORK
Please check with your university careers service for full details of local events.

MINIMUM ENTRY REQUIREMENTS
2.2 Degree

APPLICATION DEADLINE
7th January 2020

FURTHER INFORMATION
www.Top100GraduateEmployers.com
Register now for the latest news, campus events, work experience and graduate vacancies at Local Government.

Local Government Association
NATIONAL GRADUATE DEVELOPMENT PROGRAMME
ngdp
FOR LOCAL GOVERNMENT
Real life. Real work. Your opportunity to make a difference.
The ngdp is local government's fast track management training programme, enabling you to make a measurable difference from day one.
www.local.gov.uk/ngdp I @ngdp_LGA I #ngdp22

As Europe's largest employer with an annual budget of over £100 billion, there is no other organisation on Earth quite like the NHS. With the ability to have a positive impact on 56 million people, the NHS Graduate Management Training Scheme really is nothing less than a life-defining experience.

Being on this scheme is unquestionably hard work, but this multi-award winning, fast-track development scheme will enable graduates to become the healthcare leaders of the future. Graduates specialise in one of six areas: finance, general management, human resources, health informatics, policy & strategy and health analysis.

As graduates grow personally and professionally, they'll gain specialist skills while receiving full support from a dedicated mentor at Executive level. Every graduate joining the Scheme will experience a comprehensive learning and development package designed by some of the most experienced and expert learning providers in the UK. Success is granted only to those who are prepared to give their heart and soul to their profession.

The responsibility of the NHS demands that their future leaders have the tenacity, the focus, and the determination to deliver nothing but the best. Because the scheme offers a fast-track route to a senior-level role, graduates will soon find themselves facing complex problems head on and tackling high profile situations.

Working for the NHS means standing up to high levels of public scrutiny and having decisions closely inspected. Graduates who want to succeed will need to be thick-skinned, resilient and able to respond to constant change. This is a career where the hard work and unfaltering commitment of graduates not only affects the lives of others, but will ultimately define their own.

Norton Rose Fulbright provides the world's pre-eminent corporations and financial institutions with a full business law service. They have more than 4,000 lawyers and other legal staff based in Europe, the United States, Canada, Latin America, Asia, Australia, the Middle East and Africa.

Recognised for their industry focus, they are strong across all the key industry sectors: financial institutions; energy; infrastructure, mining and commodities; transport; technology and innovation; and life sciences and healthcare. Through their global risk advisory group, they leverage their industry experience with their knowledge of legal, regulatory, compliance and governance issues to provide their clients with practical solutions to the legal and regulatory risks facing their businesses.

Wherever they are, they operate in accordance with their global business principles of quality, unity and integrity. They aim to provide the highest possible standard of legal service in each of their offices and to maintain that level of quality at every point of contact.

Norton Rose Fulbright looks for intelligent, ambitious, internationally focused and commercially-minded individuals to drive their business. They will expect new joiners to think creatively and find new ways to solve problems. They expect their trainees to deliver work that meets the highest professional, ethical and business standards for their clients. All applicants must have achieved at least AAB in their A levels or equivalent and be on course to achieve (or to have achieved already) a 2.1 degree or above.

The firm offers training contracts; winter, spring and summer vacation schemes and first year opportunities for law and non-law students. Find out more about these opportunities on their website.

GRADUATE VACANCIES IN 2020
LAW

NUMBER OF VACANCIES
Up to 45 graduate jobs
For training contracts starting in 2022.

LOCATIONS OF VACANCIES

STARTING SALARY FOR 2020
See website for details.

UNIVERSITY VISITS IN 2019-20
BIRMINGHAM, BRISTOL, CAMBRIDGE, DURHAM, EDINBURGH, EXETER, KING'S COLLEGE LONDON, LEEDS, LEICESTER, LONDON SCHOOL OF ECONOMICS, MANCHESTER, NEWCASTLE, NOTTINGHAM, OXFORD, QUEEN MARY LONDON, SHEFFIELD, UNIVERSITY COLLEGE LONDON, WARWICK, YORK
Please check with your university careers service for full details of local events.

MINIMUM ENTRY REQUIREMENTS
2.1 Degree

APPLICATION DEADLINE
See website for details.

FURTHER INFORMATION
www.Top100GraduateEmployers.com
Register now for the latest news, campus events, work experience and graduate vacancies at Norton Rose Fulbright.

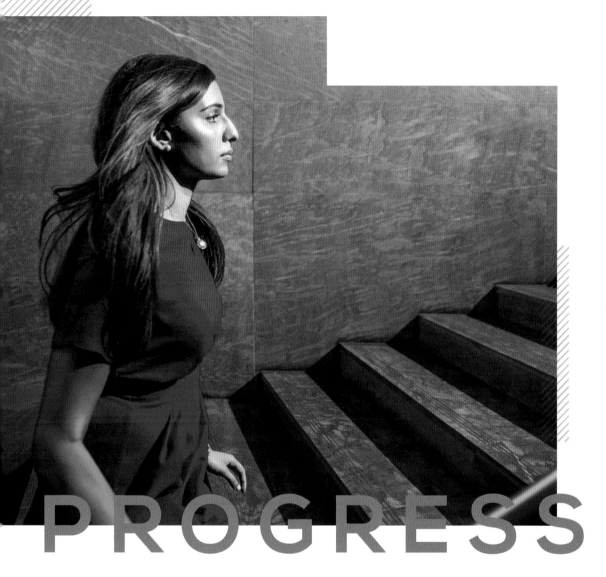

NORTON ROSE FULBRIGHT

PROGRESS
WITH PURPOSE

How do you know when you're making progress? It's all about the firsts. First day. First client. First deal closed. First mistake, and what you learned from it. It's the little steps as well as the big ones. And here's one for you now: first encounter with your future. Find out about our training contracts and vacation schemes at:

nortonrosefulbrightgraduates.com

Penguin Random House UK connects the world with the stories, ideas and writing that matter. As the biggest publisher in the UK, the diversity of its publishing includes brands such as Jamie Oliver, James Patterson and Peppa Pig through to literary prize winners such as Zadie Smith and Richard Flanagan.

Career opportunities range from the creative teams in Editorial, Marketing, Publicity and Design through to teams in Digital, Finance, Technology, Sales and Publishing Operations, to name but a few.

Their flagship entry-level programme, 'The Scheme' focuses on finding new talents for different roles each year – from marketing and publicity, to editorial.

Whether someone is motivated by working on something new, or taking the next step in their career, Penguin Random House is committed to creating an environment, and the opportunities, for their employees to do the best work of their lives.

Penguin Random House has nine publishing houses, each distinct, with their own imprints, markets and identity, including a fast-growing Audio publishing division.

They work with a wide range of talent – from storytellers, animators and developers to entrepreneurs, toy manufacturers, producers and, of course, writers. Just like broadcasters, they find increasingly different ways to bring stories and ideas to life.

Penguin Random House UK has three publishing sites in London – Vauxhall Bridge Road, Strand and Ealing Broadway; distribution centres in Frating, Grantham and Rugby; and a number of regional offices. They employ over 2,000 people in the UK.

GRADUATE VACANCIES IN 2020

MARKETING

MEDIA

SALES

NUMBER OF VACANCIES
200+ entry-level roles

LOCATIONS OF VACANCIES

STARTING SALARY FOR 2020
£23,000

UNIVERSITY VISITS IN 2019-20
Please check with your university careers service for full details of local events.

APPLICATION DEADLINE
Year-round recruitment
Early application advised.

FURTHER INFORMATION
www.Top100GraduateEmployers.com
Register now for the latest news, campus events, work experience and graduate vacancies at Penguin Random House.

Your Story Starts Here

Finding a great story - editor, publisher, sales director, finance team. Making it look good - designer, copy writer, art director, illustrator. Making the finished book - production controller, product manager, quality controller. Getting it out there - marketing assistant, publicity manager, sales executive, social media manager.

Come and be part of the first of a new kind of publisher that captures the attention of the world through the stories, ideas and writing that matter.

Penguin
Random House
UK

Pinsent Masons

Pinsent Masons is an international law firm with a reputation for delivering high-quality legal advice, rooted in its deep understanding of the sectors and geographies in which our clients operate. The firm employs over 3,000 people worldwide, including around 1,800 lawyers and 450 partners.

Pinsent Masons is a global 100 law firm, with a sector-led approach specialising in the energy, infrastructure, financial services, real estate and advanced manufacturing and technology sectors.

The firm's international footprint encompasses eight offices across Asia Pacific, two offices in the Middle East, fifteen offices in continental Europe and one in Africa. Pinsent Masons also has comprehensive coverage across each of the UK's three legal jurisdictions.

Penultimate year law students, or final year non-law students, can apply for the Vacation Placement. Over the course of a number of weeks, attendees will be fully immersed in all aspects of working life at Pinsent Masons. Placement students will experience a structured programme of work-based learning, skills training and presentations, as well as plenty of socialising and networking. The programme is available across all of our UK offices.

Pinsent Masons' two-year Training Contract comprises four six-month seats, spent in different Practice Groups, and combines regulatory and skills training. Seat allocations take account of trainees' preferences and aim to strike a balance between their choices and the firm's requirements. In each seat, trainees will be supervised by a senior colleague who will guide them through their learning and development. There is also full support from Pinsent Masons' Graduate Development team, who will meet trainees regularly to discuss their on-going performance.

GRADUATE VACANCIES IN 2020
LAW

NUMBER OF VACANCIES
60-70 graduate jobs
For training contracts starting in 2022.

LOCATIONS OF VACANCIES

STARTING SALARY FOR 2020
£23,000-£41,000
Plus a comprehensive benefits package.

UNIVERSITY VISITS IN 2019-20
ABERDEEN, ASTON, BELFAST, BIRMINGHAM, BRISTOL, CAMBRIDGE, CITY, TRINITY COLLEGE DUBLIN, UNIVERSITY COLLEGE DUBLIN, DUNDEE, DURHAM, EDINBURGH, EXETER, GLASGOW, HULL, KING'S COLLEGE LONDON, LANCASTER, LEEDS, LEICESTER, LIVERPOOL, LONDON SCHOOL OF ECONOMICS, MANCHESTER, NEWCASTLE, NOTTINGHAM, OXFORD, QUEEN MARY LONDON, SCHOOL OF AFRICAN STUDIES, SHEFFIELD, STRATHCLYDE, ULSTER, UNIVERSITY COLLEGE LONDON, WARWICK, YORK
Please check with your university careers service for full details of local events.

MINIMUM ENTRY REQUIREMENTS
2.1 Degree
120 UCAS points
300+ UCAS points for those who passed exams before 2017.

APPLICATION DEADLINE
Varies by function

FURTHER INFORMATION
www.Top100GraduateEmployers.com
Register now for the latest news, campus events, work experience and graduate vacancies at Pinsent Masons.

TAKE THE LAW INTO YOUR OWN HANDS

We're not just one of The Times Top 100 Graduate Employers, we also continue to move up the ranks. Last year, we were The Lawyer's Law Firm of the Year and our people around the world continue to work together to realise our even bigger ambitions. So there's nowhere better to take your legal career into your own hands.

Our training contracts are unlike any other: giving you experience-building responsibility and client exposure, supported by personalised career coaching that's unique to Pinsent Masons.

It all begins with a comprehensive induction to get you off to the confident start essential to making the most of the career paths open to you across the UK and around the world.

Ready to start as you mean to go on?

pinsentmasons.com/graduates

#takethelaw

POLICE:NOW
INFLUENCE FOR GENERATIONS

policenow.org.uk

graduates@policenow.org.uk

instagram.com/PoliceNowGraduates   facebook.com/PoliceNow

youtube.com/PoliceNowChangeTheStory   linkedin.com/company/police-now

> "I have a
> community to
> watch over,
> listen to and
> support."

PC Mtitimila,
Police Now neighbourhood police officer.

Police Now's National Graduate Leadership Programme offers outstanding graduates the opportunity to pursue a highly ambitious vision for social change. Its aim? To break the intergenerational cycle of crime in the most challenged areas by creating safe, confident communities in which people can thrive.

This two-year programme operates at pace and intensity. And the challenge is unique. Graduates become fully warranted neighbourhood police officers with responsibility for an area that could be home to as many as 20,000 people. They get to know their communities – the problems, the prominent offenders and the crime hotspots within them. And right from the beginning, they are expected to use innovative ideas and tactics to tackle the toughest problems and deliver high impact results.

The programme is challenging, but graduates are supported by mentors, coaches and line managers. Frontline training is delivered by over 40 different experts and a whole range of operational police officers. Opportunities to undertake prestigious secondments with Police Now's partner organisations give graduates exposure to a wide range of industries and sectors. The skills and experience that graduates gain throughout the Police Now programme ensures that they are highly in demand, whether they choose to stay in policing or pursue a career elsewhere.

This is a challenge that extends beyond the basic mission of the police to prevent crime and disorder. It's the chance to be a leader in society and on the policing frontline.

As Police Now is expanding to work with over 25 forces across England and Wales, there are even more opportunities for outstanding graduates to step forward and change the story, not just today but for generations to come.

GRADUATE VACANCIES IN 2020
POLICING

NUMBER OF VACANCIES
350 graduate jobs

LOCATIONS OF VACANCIES

STARTING SALARY FOR 2020
£23,500
Average starting salary for 2019 cohort.

UNIVERSITY VISITS IN 2019-20
BIRMINGHAM, BRISTOL, CAMBRIDGE, DURHAM, ESSEX, EXETER, HULL, KING'S COLLEGE LONDON, LEEDS, LEICESTER, LIVERPOOL, LONDON SCHOOL OF ECONOMICS, MANCHESTER, NEWCASTLE, NOTTINGHAM, NOTTINGHAM TRENT, OXFORD, QUEEN MARY LONDON, SHEFFIELD, SOUTHAMPTON, SURREY, UEA, UNIVERSITY COLLEGE LONDON, WARWICK, YORK
Please check with your university careers service for full details of local events.

MINIMUM ENTRY REQUIREMENTS
2.2 Degree
Plus a C grade in English at GCSE.

APPLICATION DEADLINE
March 2020

FURTHER INFORMATION
www.Top100GraduateEmployers.com
Register now for the latest news, campus events, work experience and graduate vacancies at **Police Now.**

You'll be there
Visible, reliable, proud

Society needs talented neighbourhood police officers as diverse as the communities they serve. Are you ready to lead change so that even the most vulnerable can thrive?

If you want to be a leader who improves the lives of those around you, apply for Police Now's National Graduate Leadership Programme today and develop skills for life.

Join us. Change the story.
policenow.org.uk

POLICE:NOW
INFLUENCE FOR GENERATIONS

Police Now is proud that of its 435 offer holders for the 2019 cohort, 54% are female, 46% are male, 20% are BAME and 14% identify as LGBT+.

The opportunity
of a lifetime

pwc

Opportunities are at the heart of a career with PwC. PwC's purpose is to build trust in society and solve important problems for their clients, helping them tackle business challenges and improving how they work. Graduates can join Actuarial, Audit, Consulting, Deals, Legal, Risk Assurance, Tax or Technology.

PwC's aim is to be 'the leading professional services firm', and to achieve this they must be innovative, responsible and attract outstanding people. With 20,000 employees at offices UK-wide, attracting the right talent continues to be paramount and, as a progressive employer, PwC continues to develop a diverse and agile workforce who feel empowered to be the best they can be. This includes supporting different ways of working, with 'Everyday Flexibility' allowing PwC people to better balance work and life, and 'dress for your day', where employees decide what's appropriate given their daily responsibilities.

At PwC, graduates and undergraduates can expect to be part of a stimulating environment working on challenging projects where they have access to a world of opportunity and experiences, in a culture that embraces difference. No matter what their degree or background, PwC have a range of roles to suit everyone.

PwC looks for talented graduates eager to learn, with business awareness, intellectual and cultural curiosity and the ability to build strong relationships. Trainees can develop and grow within a supportive and nurturing learning environment - in some business areas, this could mean working towards a professional qualification.

Whatever the route, PwC is focused on its people achieving their full potential, where hard work and accomplishments are recognised and rewarded with a competitive salary and a tailored, flexible benefits scheme.

Apply Now. Take the opportunity of a lifetime.

GRADUATE VACANCIES IN 2020
ACCOUNTANCY
CONSULTING
FINANCE
LAW
TECHNOLOGY

NUMBER OF VACANCIES
1,350 graduate jobs

LOCATIONS OF VACANCIES

STARTING SALARY FOR 2020
£Competitive
Plus a flexible benefits scheme.

MINIMUM ENTRY REQUIREMENTS
2.1 Degree

UNIVERSITY VISITS IN 2019-20
ABERDEEN, ABERYSTWYTH, ASTON, BANGOR, BATH, BELFAST, BIRMINGHAM, BRADFORD, BRISTOL, BRUNEL, CAMBRIDGE, CARDIFF, CITY, DUNDEE, DURHAM, EDINBURGH, ESSEX, EXETER, GLASGOW, HERIOT-WATT, HULL, IMPERIAL COLLEGE LONDON, KEELE, KING'S COLLEGE LONDON, KENT, LANCASTER, LEEDS, LEICESTER, LIVERPOOL, LONDON SCHOOL OF ECONOMICS, LOUGHBOROUGH, MANCHESTER, NEWCASTLE, NORTHUMBRIA, NOTTINGHAM, NOTTINGHAM TRENT, OXFORD, OXFORD BROOKES, PLYMOUTH, QUEEN MARY LONDON, READING, ROYAL HOLLOWAY, SCHOOL OF AFRICAN STUDIES, SHEFFIELD, SOUTHAMPTON, ST ANDREWS, STIRLING, STRATHCLYDE, SURREY, SUSSEX, SWANSEA, UEA, ULSTER, UNIVERSITY COLLEGE LONDON, WARWICK, YORK
Please check with your university careers service for full details of local events.

APPLICATION DEADLINE
Varies by function

FURTHER INFORMATION
www.Top100GraduateEmployers.com
Register now for the latest news, campus events, work experience and graduate vacancies at PwC.

Your career starts here

We welcome all degree subjects. Surprised? Don't be. We see your degree as just the start. It's your first step in taking your career in all sorts of directions. If you're passionate about business and eager to learn, we'll help you excel in your career. Join us in Actuarial, Audit, Consulting, Deals, Legal, Risk Assurance, Tax or Technology.

Visit here to find out more:
pwc.co.uk/careers

🐦 **@pwc_uk_careers**

f **PwCCareersUK**

in **pwc-uk**

⊙ **pwc_uk_careers**

▶ **careerspwc**

Valuing Difference. Driving Inclusion.

✸✸ RBS

GRADUATE VACANCIES IN 2020

FINANCE

HUMAN RESOURCES

MARKETING

TECHNOLOGY

NUMBER OF VACANCIES
250+ graduate jobs

LOCATIONS OF VACANCIES

RBS brands are some of the best-known names in the financial services industry – The Royal Bank of Scotland, NatWest, Coutts, Adam & Company, Ulster Bank, Lombard and many more. They serve over 19 million customers with all their banking needs, and their headquarters are in Edinburgh.

RBS is a great place for graduates and interns to start their career – they're important to the bank's future, so in return RBS will give them a fulfilling role, fair pay, good leadership and excellent training.

To be ready for the future, RBS need the right people, with the right skills, doing the right work. Their five Critical People Capabilities™ will make sure everyone joining one of their programmes will develop the right skills, helping them build the bank of the future. Those capabilities are: Improver Innovator, Change Ready, Critical Thinker, Connected and Trusted Advisor.

The progressive and structured approach to career development at RBS means graduates and interns will help change the bank for the better. A graduate's career path is theirs to choose, and RBS believe the journey and experiences along the way are every bit as important as where their paths ultimately lead.

RBS truly focus on career development and help graduates and interns 'find their path'. They also help build skills in lots of different ways, like: mentoring, entrepreneurial training, professional qualifications, coaching, rotations, charity work, technical training and development, agile working and flexible learning.

Life isn't linear, and all the programmes at RBS let graduates and interns explore their different business areas – the only question is: which pathway will candidates choose?

STARTING SALARY FOR 2020
£31,850

UNIVERSITY VISITS IN 2019-20
DURHAM, EDINBURGH, GLASGOW, HERIOT-WATT, LEEDS, MANCHESTER, NOTTINGHAM, QUEEN MARY LONDON, SHEFFIELD, ST ANDREWS, STRATHCLYDE, UNIVERSITY COLLEGE LONDON, WARWICK
Please check with your university careers service for full details of local events.

MINIMUM ENTRY REQUIREMENTS
2.1 Degree
STEM degree required for Software Engineering roles.

APPLICATION DEADLINE
31st December 2019
Please see website for details.

FURTHER INFORMATION
www.Top100GraduateEmployers.com
*Register now for the latest news, campus events, work experience and graduate vacancies at **RBS**.*

Find your path.

Life isn't linear.
We don't expect your career path to be either.

If you're interested in finding out more about our opportunities,
visit www.jobs.rbs.com

❈ **RBS** Graduates & Interns

GRADUATE VACANCIES IN 2020

ENGINEERING

NUMBER OF VACANCIES
Up to 300 graduate jobs

LOCATIONS OF VACANCIES

Vacancies also available in Europe, the USA, and Asia.

From building the world's most efficient large aero-engine to supporting NASA missions on the edge of space, Rolls-Royce transforms the potential of technology. A career with Rolls-Royce means creating cleaner, faster, more competitive power; looking to the future, and shaping the world we live in.

Rolls-Royce pioneers cutting-edge technologies that deliver the cleanest, safest and most competitive solutions to meet the planet's vital power needs – in the air, on land and at sea. Rolls-Royce's power comes from its people; 54,500 across over 50 international offices who make it one of the world's leading industrial technology companies.

The company invests well over £1.4 billion each year in research and development, and files for more patents per year than any other company in the UK. At the same time, at Rolls-Royce each and every member of the team is encouraged to be themselves. The company believes that diverse ways of thinking make for better, bolder ideas – pioneers do things differently. They know that the next big innovation could come from the smallest fragment of inspiration.

Rolls-Royce has opportunities for graduates in diverse engineering and manufacturing engineering specialisms. Across every programme, Rolls-Royce looks for agile people who are creative, analytical, innovative and enthusiastic. Individuals who are open-minded and can bring fresh perspectives to enduring challenges.

A career at Rolls-Royce means learning from, and working with, brilliant minds – some of the foremost experts in the engineering world. Help solve complex, fascinating problems. Work on live projects in a company that's created the world's most efficient large aero-engine, powered nuclear submarines and enabled land-speed records. Help pioneer tomorrow.

STARTING SALARY FOR 2020
£28,500
Plus a £2,000 joining bonus.

UNIVERSITY VISITS IN 2019-20
BATH, BIRMINGHAM, BRISTOL, CAMBRIDGE, EDINBURGH, GLASGOW, IMPERIAL COLLEGE LONDON, LANCASTER, LIVERPOOL, LOUGHBOROUGH, MANCHESTER, NOTTINGHAM, NOTTINGHAM TRENT, OXFORD, SHEFFIELD, SOUTHAMPTON, STRATHCLYDE, WARWICK
Please check with your university careers service for full details of local events.

MINIMUM ENTRY REQUIREMENTS
2.1 Degree

APPLICATION DEADLINE
Year-round recruitment
Early application advised.

FURTHER INFORMATION
www.Top100GraduateEmployers.com
Register now for the latest news, campus events, work experience and graduate vacancies at Rolls-Royce.

Be bold
& Free the flip flop

Internship and graduate opportunities

Whether it's creating cleaner, safer energy or helping people to break out their beach gear via the world's most efficient aero-engines, we pioneer the power that matters. To find out how you could help shape the world we live in, visit **careers.rolls-royce.com**

Beyond tomorrow

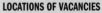

raf.mod.uk/recruitment

facebook.com/RAFrecruitment **f**

linkedin.com/company/royal-air-force **in**   twitter.com/RAF_recruitment **y**

instagram.com/RAFrecruitment **⊙**   youtube.com/RoyalAirForce **▶**

○ ROYAL AIR FORCE

With cutting-edge technology, hundreds of aircraft and more than 30,000 active personnel, the Royal Air Force (RAF) is a key part of the British Armed Forces, defending the UK and its interests, strengthening international peace and stability, as well as being a force for good in the world.

Its people lie at the heart of the RAF; they're looking for professionalism, dedication and courage to achieve the RAF's vision of being 'an agile, adaptable and capable Air Force that, person for person, is second to none, and that makes a decisive air power contribution in support of the UK Defence Mission'.

The world is continually changing and so the RAF must change in order to meet the challenges of the 21st century. The RAF has become a smaller and more dynamic force, able to deliver capability all over the world; be that in support of combat missions or humanitarian aid and disaster relief. Whilst the exploitation of cutting-edge technologies helps meet these challenges; it is essential that the RAF continues to recruit and select high calibre graduates, for officer roles, to lead the RAF of tomorrow.

Graduates joining the RAF, in an Officer role, have been selected because they have demonstrated that they have the potential to be a leader. As an Officer they will be expected to lead and manage the women and men, for whom they are responsible, to meet the RAF's challenges of today and tomorrow. The world-class training that RAF Officers will receive ensures that they are equipped to do this. There are more than twenty different graduate career opportunities, including Engineering, Aircrew, Logistics and Personnel roles, as well as medical opportunities for qualified doctors, nurses and dentists. In return, the RAF offers a competitive salary, free medical & dental services, travel opportunities and world-class training. It's no ordinary job.

GRADUATE VACANCIES IN 2020

ENGINEERING

HUMAN RESOURCES

LAW

LOGISTICS

TECHNOLOGY

NUMBER OF VACANCIES
500-600 graduate jobs

LOCATIONS OF VACANCIES

STARTING SALARY FOR 2020
£32,780
Starting salary after Initial Officer Training (six months).

UNIVERSITY VISITS IN 2019-20
ABERDEEN, BATH, BELFAST, BIRMINGHAM, BRADFORD, BRISTOL, BRUNEL, CAMBRIDGE, CARDIFF, CITY, DUNDEE, DURHAM, EDINBURGH, ESSEX, EXETER, GLASGOW, HULL, KENT, LANCASTER, LEEDS, LEICESTER, LIVERPOOL, LOUGHBOROUGH, MANCHESTER, NEWCASTLE, NORTHUMBRIA, NOTTINGHAM, NOTTINGHAM TRENT, OXFORD, PLYMOUTH, READING, SHEFFIELD, SOUTHAMPTON, ST ANDREWS, STIRLING, STRATHCLYDE, SURREY, SUSSEX, SWANSEA, UEA, ULSTER, YORK
Please check with your university careers service for full details of local events.

MINIMUM ENTRY REQUIREMENTS
Relevant degree required for some roles.

APPLICATION DEADLINE
Year-round recruitment
Early application advised.

FURTHER INFORMATION
www.Top100GraduateEmployers.com
Register now for the latest news, campus events, work experience and graduate vacancies at the Royal Air Force.

ROYAL AIR FORCE
REGULAR & RESERVE

"So you think you've got what it takes to be an officer in the RAF"

There are graduate careers and then there are graduate challenges - we'd like to think we're the latter. Our officers don't just have good promotion prospects, they get competitive pay and world-class training, as well as six weeks' paid holiday a year, subsidised food and accommodation, free healthcare, and free access to our sports facilities.

As well as specialist training, you'll learn valuable leadership and management skills; you'll also have the opportunity to take part in adventurous training such as rock climbing, skiing and sailing. As you develop your career, you'll move on to face new challenges and opportunities for promotion - both in the UK and overseas.

Interested? If you think you've got what it takes to be an Officer in the RAF, take a look at the RAF Recruitment website at the roles available, what's required for entry and the 24 week Initial Officer Training Course at RAF College Cranwell. You could also be eligible for sponsorship through your sixth-form or university courses, depending on the role you're interested in. We're currently recruiting Engineers, but have opportunities in Logistics, Medical, Personnel, Intelligence and Aircrew Officer roles. Visit the Education and Funding page of the website to find out about the opportunities available.

Healthcare in action

If you've just completed a relevant medical degree, the RAF can offer you a career filled with variety and adventure, as well as first-class postgraduate and specialist training. Once you've been accepted you'll spend 11 weeks on the Specialist Officers Initial Training Course (SOITC).

www.raf.mod.uk/recruitment/lifestyle-benefits/education-funding/

GRADUATE VACANCIES IN 2020
ENGINEERING
FINANCE
GENERAL MANAGEMENT
HUMAN RESOURCES
LAW
LOGISTICS
MEDIA
RESEARCH & DEVELOPMENT
TECHNOLOGY

NUMBER OF VACANCIES
No fixed quota

LOCATIONS OF VACANCIES

Vacancies also available elsewhere in the world.

STARTING SALARY FOR 2020
£25,984

UNIVERSITY VISITS IN 2019-20
LIVERPOOL, LOUGHBOROUGH, PLYMOUTH, STRATHCLYDE, SWANSEA
Please check with your university careers service for full details of local events.

MINIMUM ENTRY REQUIREMENTS
Relevant degree required for some roles.

APPLICATION DEADLINE
Year-round recruitment

FURTHER INFORMATION
www.Top100GraduateEmployers.com
Register now for the latest news, campus events, work experience and graduate vacancies at the Royal Navy.

Throughout the course of history, a life at sea has always attracted those with a taste for travel and adventure; but there are plenty of other reasons for graduates and final-year students to consider a challenging and wide-ranging career with the Royal Navy.

The Royal Navy is, first and foremost, a fighting force. Serving alongside Britain's allies in conflicts around the world, it also vitally protects UK ports, fishing grounds and merchant ships, helping to combat international smuggling, terrorism and piracy. Increasingly, its 30,000 personnel are involved in humanitarian and relief missions; situations where their skills, discipline and resourcefulness make a real difference to people's lives.

Graduates are able to join the Royal Navy as Officers – the senior leadership and management team in the various branches, which range from engineering, air and warfare to medical, the Fleet Air Arm and logistics. Starting salaries of at least £25,984 – rising to £31,232 in the first year – compare well with those in industry.

Those wanting to join the Royal Navy as an Engineer – with Marine, Weapon or Air Engineer Officer, above or below the water – could work on anything from sensitive electronics to massive gas-turbine engines and nuclear weapons. What's more, the Royal Navy can offer a secure, flexible career and the potential to extend to age 50.

The Royal Navy offers opportunities for early responsibility, career development, sport, recreation and travel which exceed any in civilian life. With its global reach and responsibilities, the Royal Navy still offers plenty of adventure and the chance to see the world, while pursuing one of the most challenging, varied and fulfilling careers available.

YOU MAKE A DIFFERENCE NOT MAKE UP THE NUMBERS

ROYAL NAVY OFFICER

Being an officer in the Royal Navy is a career like any other, but the circumstances and places are sometimes extraordinary. With opportunities ranging from Engineer Officer to Medical Officer, it's a responsible, challenging career that will take you further than you've been before. If you want more than just a job, join the Royal Navy and live a life without limits.

LIFE WITHOUT LIMITS
08456 07 55 55
ROYALNAVY.MOD.UK/CAREERS

Santander

santanderjobs.co.uk/realiseyourfuture

emergingtalent@santander.co.uk

Santander is one of the largest and most successful financial groups in the world, and their ambition is to become the best bank for their customers, investors and employees. They recognise technology is changing how customers bank and pay and are working to be at the forefront of that change.

Santander are motivated by having the customer at the heart of what they do. Strong teamwork, an innovative approach to technology, market-leading incentive packages, and a culture of support ensure graduates deliver their personal best, every day. Santander focuses on giving graduates everything they need to be the best they can be in their chosen areas. They are supported in this throughout their programmes, working in an agile and dynamic way within a fast-paced, diverse environment.

Graduate programmes within the business are run across different specialisms and business areas, each designed to give an in-depth understanding of what makes Santander tick. That could mean developing innovative products for their customers, identifying ways to improve processes for colleagues, or building relationships with high-profile clients. In everything that graduates do at Santander, they are continually focused on ensuring that Santander progresses to become a truly digital bank.

What's more, graduates will be part of a structured development scheme split into four learning cycles that usually ends with an industry-recognised qualification in their chosen area.

Through these programmes graduates will have all of the support they need in order to succeed, with a dedicated graduate manager as well as continuous development – there's plenty of benefits and no shortage of opportunities to grow with Santander.

Your future at the heart of our business

Our Emerging Talent schemes provide everything you'll need to realise your future. We're here to help people and businesses prosper and you'll be at the heart of that change, whilst placing the customer at the heart of everything we do.

So, if you're passionate about making our banking products, services and tools simple, personal and fair, whilst helping Santander to become the leading digital bank, we have a scheme for you.

Realise your future, apply today: www.santanderjobs.co.uk/realiseyourfuture

GRADUATE VACANCIES IN 2020

ENGINEERING

FINANCE

GENERAL MANAGEMENT

HUMAN RESOURCES

MARKETING

RESEARCH & DEVELOPMENT

SALES

TECHNOLOGY

NUMBER OF VACANCIES
40+ graduate jobs

LOCATIONS OF VACANCIES

Vacancies also available elsewhere in the world.

STARTING SALARY FOR 2020
£Competitive
Plus a competitive bonus and benefits.

Shell is an international energy company that aims to meet the world's growing need for more and cleaner energy solutions in ways that are economically, environmentally and socially responsible. They are one of the world's largest independent energy companies, operating in more than 70 countries.

At Shell, the work ranges from developing advanced fuels to improving data processing within the IT industry.

They have many roles in technical and commercial industries that are open to both fresh graduates and professionals.

The structured Graduate Programme is designed to provide graduates with the business knowledge and training required to enhance their career and become a future leader.

Depending on their chosen path, graduates will participate in a 2-5 year development programme. This will include 2 or 3 rotations that combine on-the-job learning with formal training opportunities. Every step of the way graduates are given comprehensive support from mentors, supervisors, work buddies and the graduate network.

The Assessed Internship is an excellent way to get to know Shell from the inside. Lasting typically 10-12 weeks, students will join a real project with a significant level of business impact. Supported by a mentor and supervisor throughout, this is an opportunity to discover new skills, build a network and gain insight into the business.

Shell believes in creating an inclusive culture where their employees can thrive. To power progress together, they are focused on attracting and developing the brightest minds.

Be part of the future of energy. Be part of Shell.

UNIVERSITY VISITS IN 2019-20
ABERDEEN, CAMBRIDGE, HERIOT-WATT,
IMPERIAL COLLEGE LONDON, LEEDS,
LONDON SCHOOL OF ECONOMICS,
MANCHESTER, OXFORD, STRATHCLYDE,
UNIVERSITY COLLEGE LONDON
Please check with your university careers service for full details of local events.

APPLICATION DEADLINE
Varies by function

FURTHER INFORMATION
www.Top100GraduateEmployers.com
*Register now for the latest news, campus events, work experience and graduate vacancies at **Shell**.*

WE HELP YOU DO

BIG
THINGS

IN THE SHELL GRADUATE PROGRAMME

SIEMENS
Ingenuity for life

siemens.co.uk/grads

facebook.com/SiemensUKnews
linkedin.com/company/siemens
twitter.com/SiemensUKjobs
instagram.com/Siemens_UK
youtube.com/Siemens

Siemens is a global technology and engineering powerhouse that works across an incredible breadth of industries and sectors. The company describes itself as being here, there and everywhere. Just one look around the modern world is enough to see why.

Siemens is a leader in manufacturing, power generation and the Smart Infrastructure that creates cities and communities. It is driving digital transformation at the forefront of Industry 4.0, and developing a range of futuristic technologies like AI, robotics, driverless cars and MindSphere, a powerful insight into how future cities will connect to the Internet of Things.

For forward-thinking graduates, Siemens' scale of ambition and breadth of expertise are major attractions. New starters can expect to be on the ground, participating in meaningful, cutting-edge projects. The culture revolves around ingenuity and inclusion, with down-to-earth collaboration that promotes innovation and invention. The company ensures graduates feel they are listened to; employees have a voice from the moment they step through the doors.

The company employs over 15,000 people across 25 major offices and 13 manufacturing sites in the UK. That means opportunities all over the country. There are also roles on offer across a wide range of fields. Siemens employs the brightest engineers and business minds in positions from electrical and mechanical engineering, through to project management and finance.

Crucially, everyone benefits from a structured two-year Graduate Development Programme, which grows the core and soft skills essential for a successful Siemens career. Siemens places a big value on inclusivity and individuality, through tailored programmes that reflect personal interests and ambitions.

GRADUATE VACANCIES IN 2020
ENGINEERING
FINANCE
GENERAL MANAGEMENT
PURCHASING
RESEARCH & DEVELOPMENT
SALES
TECHNOLOGY

NUMBER OF VACANCIES
70-80 graduate jobs

LOCATIONS OF VACANCIES

STARTING SALARY FOR 2020
£28,000

MINIMUM ENTRY REQUIREMENTS
Relevant degree required for some roles.

UNIVERSITY VISITS IN 2019-20
ASTON, BATH, BIRMINGHAM, CAMBRIDGE, IMPERIAL COLLEGE LONDON, LOUGHBOROUGH, MANCHESTER, NEWCASTLE, NOTTINGHAM, OXFORD, SHEFFIELD, SOUTHAMPTON, STRATHCLYDE, WARWICK, YORK
Please check with your university careers service for full details of local events.

APPLICATION DEADLINE
Early January 2020

FURTHER INFORMATION
www.Top100GraduateEmployers.com
Register now for the latest news, campus events, work experience and graduate vacancies at Siemens.

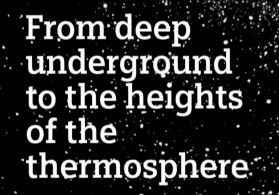

skyearlycareers.com
earlycareers@sky.uk
twitter.com/EarlyCareersSky   facebook.com/EarlyCareersSky

Sky is Europe's biggest entertainment brand, connecting 23.7 million customers across seven countries with products and services they love. What's behind the top-quality shows, innovative tech and must-have packages? Talented, dedicated and supportive people.

From software developers to finance professionals. From technical geniuses to marketing gurus. Sky is a place where people from all walks of life get freedom and support to do their best work. At Sky, graduates will do much more than contribute to delivering world-class content. They will have freedom to think of new ideas. Get support and training to make them happen.

There are so many ways for graduates to make an impact at Sky. Want to learn how to be a business leader? Develop cutting-edge products? Gain skills across the business or become an expert in a specialist area? The range of graduate programmes here means new joiners have the chance to do all this and more.

Sky also offer lots of insight days and summer internships to help graduates decide what kind of career would suit them best.

Whatever they do, they'll be working in a fun, fast-moving environment. Surrounded by some of the best people in the industry. Benefiting from on-the-job learning. Enjoying the opportunity to try out new ideas and shape where the business goes next. They'll also get to see and do things at Sky that they simply wouldn't experience anywhere else. Who knows? They might bump into Anthony Joshua in reception or work on a product that changes how millions of people watch their favourite shows.

Joining Sky as a graduate gives them the space to be whoever they are, and a job they love to talk about.

GRADUATE VACANCIES IN 2020

CONSULTING
FINANCE
MARKETING
TECHNOLOGY

NUMBER OF VACANCIES
175 graduate jobs

LOCATIONS OF VACANCIES

STARTING SALARY FOR 2020
£28,000-£35,000

UNIVERSITY VISITS IN 2019-20
ASTON, BATH, BIRMINGHAM, BRISTOL, BRUNEL, CAMBRIDGE, CARDIFF, CITY, DURHAM, EDINBURGH, EXETER, IMPERIAL COLLEGE LONDON, KING'S COLLEGE LONDON, LEEDS, LIVERPOOL, LOUGHBOROUGH, MANCHESTER, NEWCASTLE, NOTTINGHAM, OXFORD, QUEEN MARY LONDON, READING, ROYAL HOLLOWAY, SHEFFIELD, SOUTHAMPTON, STRATHCLYDE, SURREY, UNIVERSITY COLLEGE LONDON, WARWICK, YORK
Please check with your university careers service for full details of local events.

APPLICATION DEADLINE
Varies by function

FURTHER INFORMATION
www.Top100GraduateEmployers.com
*Register now for the latest news, campus events, work experience and graduate vacancies at **Sky**.*

SLAUGHTER AND MAY

slaughterandmay.com

trainee.recruit@slaughterandmay.com

Slaughter and May is one of the most prestigious law firms in the world. They advise high-profile and often landmark international transactions. Their excellent and varied client list ranges from governments to entrepreneurs, from retailers to entertainment companies, and from conglomerates to Premier League football clubs.

Slaughter and May has offices in London, Beijing, Brussels and Hong Kong, plus relationship firms in all the major jurisdictions. Slaughter and May has built a reputation for delivering innovative solutions to difficult problems. They are a full service law firm to corporate clients, and have leading practitioners across a wide range of practice areas including mergers and acquisitions, corporate and commercial, financing, tax, competition, dispute resolution, real estate, pensions and employment, financial regulation, information technology and intellectual property.

Their lawyers are not set billing or time targets, and are therefore free to concentrate on what matters most – expertise, sound judgement, a willingness to help one another and the highest quality of client service.

During the two-year training contract, trainees turn their hand to a broad range of work, taking an active role in four, five or six groups while sharing an office with a partner or experienced associate. All trainees spend at least two six-month seats in the firm's market-leading corporate, commercial and financing groups. Subject to gaining some contentious experience, they choose how to spend the remaining time.

The firm takes great store in drawing strength from diversity. With 103 different degree courses from 65 different universities, and 44 nationalities represented among our lawyers, our culture is extremely broad.

GRADUATE VACANCIES IN 2020

LAW

NUMBER OF VACANCIES
80 graduate jobs
For training contracts starting in 2022.

LOCATIONS OF VACANCIES

STARTING SALARY FOR 2020
£45,000

UNIVERSITY VISITS IN 2019-20
ABERDEEN, BIRMINGHAM, BRISTOL, CARDIFF, CAMBRIDGE, UNIVERSITY COLLEGE DUBLIN, DURHAM, EDINBURGH, EXETER, GLASGOW, KING'S COLLEGE LONDON, LANCASTER, LEEDS, LEICESTER, LONDON SCHOOL OF ECONOMICS, MANCHESTER, NEWCASTLE, NOTTINGHAM, OXFORD, QUEEN MARY LONDON, SHEFFIELD, SCHOOL OF AFRICAN STUDIES, ST ANDREWS, UNIVERSITY COLLEGE LONDON, WARWICK, YORK
Please check with your university careers service for full details of local events.

MINIMUM ENTRY REQUIREMENTS
2.1 Degree

APPLICATION DEADLINE
Please see website for full details.

FURTHER INFORMATION
www.Top100GraduateEmployers.com
*Register now for the latest news, campus events, work experience and graduate vacancies at **Slaughter and May**.*

A world of difference

Laws, international markets, global institutions… all changing every day. So how do we, as an international law firm, create the agility of mind that enables us to guide some of the world's most influential organisations into the future?

By allowing bright people the freedom to grow. By training lawyers in a way that develops a closer understanding of clients through working on a wider range of transactions. By fostering an ethos of knowledge sharing, support and mutual development by promoting from within and leaving the clocks outside when it comes to billing. To learn more about how our key differences not only make a world of difference to our clients, but also to our lawyers and their careers, visit

slaughterandmay.com/careers

SLAUGHTER AND MAY

80
training contracts

300+
workshops
and schemes

Lawyers from
65
universities

Teach First

Teach First is a charity building a fair education for all. They develop inspiring teachers and leaders who are determined to make a difference in the schools where they're needed most. Since 2002, 10,000+ talented recruits have helped to change the lives of more than a million children from poorer backgrounds.

Graduates have many career options, but few more meaningful than teaching. Teach First want graduates to choose a career that unlocks their talents and future, while unlocking the potential of the next generation. Too often, young people's futures are decided by their postcode, not their potential. Yet a timely intervention from a great teacher can raise aspirations and change lives.

Teach First's Training Programme offers immediate career momentum whilst giving trainees all the support required to succeed in the classroom. Over two years, trainees qualify as teachers and gain a fully-funded Postgraduate Diploma in Education and Leadership (PGDE). Through secondary, primary or early years placements, graduates make an instant impact on the lives of young people, in a role where no two days are ever the same.

On completion of their PGDE, more than half continue teaching in schools, with many progressing quickly to leadership roles. The charity's influential network also links trainees to organisations who value the transferable skills they bring.

The challenge is real, but so is the potential to create a lasting change. It's fun too, working with children, and alongside fellow teachers who already do a fantastic job. Along the way, trainees develop skills such as resilience and empathy that will set them up for success – whichever career path they choose. Having inspired a classroom of animated teenagers on a Friday afternoon, anything else will feel like a breeze...

GRADUATE VACANCIES IN 2020
TEACHING

NUMBER OF VACANCIES
1,750 graduate jobs

LOCATIONS OF VACANCIES

STARTING SALARY FOR 2020
£Competitive

UNIVERSITY VISITS IN 2019-20
ABERDEEN, ABERYSTWYTH, ASTON, BANGOR, BATH, BELFAST, BIRMINGHAM, BRADFORD, BRISTOL, BRUNEL, CAMBRIDGE, CARDIFF, CITY, DUNDEE, DURHAM, EDINBURGH, ESSEX, EXETER, GLASGOW, HERIOT-WATT, HULL, IMPERIAL COLLEGE LONDON, KEELE, KING'S COLLEGE LONDON, KENT, LANCASTER, LEEDS, LEICESTER, LIVERPOOL, LONDON SCHOOL OF ECONOMICS, LOUGHBOROUGH, MANCHESTER, NEWCASTLE, NORTHUMBRIA, NOTTINGHAM, NOTTINGHAM TRENT, OXFORD, OXFORD BROOKES, PLYMOUTH, QUEEN MARY LONDON, READING, ROYAL HOLLOWAY, SCHOOL OF AFRICAN STUDIES, SHEFFIELD, SOUTHAMPTON, ST ANDREWS, STIRLING, STRATHCLYDE, SURREY, SUSSEX, SWANSEA, UEA, ULSTER, UNIVERSITY COLLEGE LONDON, WARWICK, YORK
Please check with your university careers service for full details of local events.

MINIMUM ENTRY REQUIREMENTS
2.1 Degree
However, all applications are assessed on a case-by-case basis.

APPLICATION DEADLINE
Year-round recruitment
Early application advised.

FURTHER INFORMATION
www.Top100GraduateEmployers.com
*Register now for the latest news, campus events, work experience and graduate vacancies at **Teach First**.*

Monday morning

A.	Fire up the laptop. Open Excel.

B.	Fire up the classroom. Make them excel.

Learn skills that will stay with you – and your students – far beyond the classroom door. As they find their potential, you'll discover your own.

ALTER
THE
OUTCOME

The Think Ahead programme is a new route into social work for graduates and career-changers remarkable enough to make a real difference to people with mental health problems. The paid, two-year programme combines on-the-job learning, a Masters degree and leadership training.

Mental health social workers use therapy, support, and advocacy to enable people to manage the social factors in their lives – like relationships, housing, and employment – to allow them to get well and stay well.

The Think Ahead programme focuses on adult community mental health teams, supporting people living with a wide variety of illnesses such as bipolar disorder, schizophrenia, and personality disorders. These are multi-disciplinary teams, usually within an NHS Trust, which can include social workers, nurses, support workers, occupational therapists, psychologists and psychiatrists.

Participants on the programme begin their training with an intensive six-week residential over the summer. This prepares them for frontline work by giving them a grounding in approaches to mental health social work.

Following this training, participants work within NHS mental health teams in units of four. Each unit is led by a highly experienced Consultant Social Worker, and participants share responsibility for the care of the individuals they work with. Participants become professionally qualified in the second year of the programme and are then able to work more independently.

Throughout the programme there is regular training and time allocated for academic study. The programme culminates in a Masters degree in social work. Leadership training also takes place throughout the programme, supporting participants to become excellent social workers, and to work towards leading change in the future.

GRADUATE VACANCIES IN 2020
SOCIAL WORK

NUMBER OF VACANCIES
100 graduate jobs

LOCATIONS OF VACANCIES

STARTING SALARY FOR 2020
£18,200
This is a tax-free bursary.

UNIVERSITY VISITS IN 2019-20
ASTON, BIRMINGHAM, BRISTOL, CAMBRIDGE, DURHAM, KING'S COLLEGE LONDON, LEEDS, LIVERPOOL, LONDON SCHOOL OF ECONOMICS, MANCHESTER, NOTTINGHAM, OXFORD, QUEEN MARY LONDON, SHEFFIELD, SOUTHAMPTON, SUSSEX, UEA, UNIVERSITY COLLEGE LONDON, WARWICK, YORK
Please check with your university careers service for full details of local events.

MINIMUM ENTRY REQUIREMENTS
2.1 Degree

APPLICATION DEADLINE
April 2020

FURTHER INFORMATION
www.Top100GraduateEmployers.com
Register now for the latest news, campus events, work experience and graduate vacancies at Think Ahead.

THINK
AHEAD

Think Ahead has given me a deeper understanding of the impact that mental illness can have on individuals.

Jan, Edinburgh graduate
and Think Ahead participant

thinkahead.org

TPP is a global health IT company, working on cutting-edge technology to transform lives across the world. They work on pioneering products, including digital health software, apps, AI, and ground-breaking research. TPP need problem solvers from all disciplines to help them move healthcare forward.

TPP have had great success in the UK, with over 5,500 organisations using their system to support over 48 million patient records. In recent years, TPP has expanded internationally to tackle global health challenges.

The Analyst, Communications and Account teams regularly travel internationally, most recently to China and the Middle East. The technical teams also have the opportunity to travel. During these trips, staff have the time to go sightseeing and sample local cuisine.

It's not just TPP's products that are revolutionary – they've also broken the mould in terms of company culture. TPP recognise the potential that each graduate has from the moment they start, and use that talent to work on exciting projects and challenges. An employee's value at the company isn't based on how long they've been there – TPP operates on a flat hierarchy, so staff can make a difference and work on new projects from the moment they start. TPP listen to their employees and have changed the way they work based on feedback, meaning their staff can be empowered to make a difference. As a result, TPP have been consistently recognised as an outstanding graduate employer.

TPP's hands-on training approach means new employees will have plenty of responsibility from day one, with great support from the team around them, so applicants don't need to have any prior experience – coding or otherwise. A bright graduate who is full of ideas and likes spending time with some of the sharpest minds around will be well suited to a career with TPP.

GRADUATE VACANCIES IN 2020

MARKETING

RESEARCH & DEVELOPMENT

SALES

TECHNOLOGY

NUMBER OF VACANCIES
50+ graduate jobs

LOCATIONS OF VACANCIES

STARTING SALARY FOR 2020
£45,000

UNIVERSITY VISITS IN 2019-20
BATH, BIRMINGHAM, BRISTOL, CAMBRIDGE, DURHAM, EDINBURGH, IMPERIAL COLLEGE LONDON, LEEDS, MANCHESTER, OXFORD, SOUTHAMPTON, ST ANDREWS, WARWICK, YORK
Please check with your university careers service for full details of local events.

MINIMUM ENTRY REQUIREMENTS
2.1 Degree

APPLICATION DEADLINE
Year-round recruitment

FURTHER INFORMATION
www.Top100GraduateEmployers.com
*Register now for the latest news, campus events, work experience and graduate vacancies at **TPP**.*

WRITE CODE.
SOLVE PROBLEMS.
SAVE LIVES.

STARTING SALARY:

£45,000

ROLES INCLUDE:

- **Software Developer**
- **Graduate Analyst**
- **Communications Manager**
- **Account Manager**
- **Technical Operations**

NO EXPERIENCE REQUIRED

INTERNSHIPS AVAILABLE

www.tpp-careers.com

UBS

UBS works with individuals, families, institutions, and corporations to help answer some of life's questions, through award-winning wealth management advisory, investment banking and asset management expertise, or private and corporate banking services in Switzerland.

UBS are a team of more than 60,000 colleagues, collaborating across all major financial centres in more than 50 countries. They strive for excellence in everything they do, and this has awarded them recognition across their businesses. They offer a collaborative, international and diverse working environment that rewards passion, commitment and success – and are regularly recognised as an attractive employer. Together. That's how they do things.

Succeeding at UBS means respecting, understanding and trusting colleagues and clients. Challenging others and being challenged in return.

Graduates can apply to UBS's Graduate Talent Program (GTP) or Summer Internship Program. The GTP lasts 18 months and gives graduates the chance to be involved in day-to-day operations, working with professionals and gaining first-hand experience of the business. As well as on-the-job learning, they will get training on the financial markets, their products and other core business topics. Rotational assignments are a key part of the programme. By taking on other roles in related departments, graduates gain a wider perspective.

UBS's Summer Internship is a 10-week programme and gives graduates a chance to learn about the business from top to bottom, and to experience their unique workplace culture. Also, the summer internship offers the opportunity to enhance business knowledge (and network) with business speeches, community days and case studies.

GRADUATE VACANCIES IN 2020
FINANCE
HUMAN RESOURCES
INVESTMENT BANKING
MARKETING
SALES
TECHNOLOGY

NUMBER OF VACANCIES
100 graduate jobs

LOCATIONS OF VACANCIES

STARTING SALARY FOR 2020
£Competitive

UNIVERSITY VISITS IN 2019-20
BATH, CAMBRIDGE, IMPERIAL COLLEGE LONDON, KING'S COLLEGE LONDON, LONDON SCHOOL OF ECONOMICS, QUEEN MARY LONDON, UNIVERSITY COLLEGE LONDON, WARWICK
Please check with your university careers service for full details of local events.

MINIMUM ENTRY REQUIREMENTS
2.1 Degree

APPLICATION DEADLINE
Varies by function

FURTHER INFORMATION
www.Top100GraduateEmployers.com
Register now for the latest news, campus events, work experience and graduate vacancies at UBS.

Success.

Here we go.

Do you want to develop and succeed?
If you're a team player, this is a great
place to move forward – personally and
professionally. And we value and
reward performance along the way.

ubs.com/graduates

unilever.co.uk/careers/graduates

facebook.com/UnileverCareers **f**   enquiry@unilevergraduates.com ✉

linkedin.com/company/unilever **in**   twitter.com/UnileverGradsUK **y**

Unilever is a leading consumer goods company who make some of the world's best-loved brands: Dove, Knorr, Magnum, Lynx, Sure, Tresemmé, Simple and Hellmann's, to name a few. Over two billion consumers use their products every day. Unilever products are sold in 190 countries and they employ 161,000 globally.

Around the world, Unilever products help people look good, feel good and get more out of life. Unilever's vision is to grow its business, while decoupling its environmental footprint from growth and increasing positive social impact. Unilever is looking for talented graduates who can challenge the way things are done, bring new ideas to the table, and dare to make big decisions to help achieve this ambition.

Graduates can apply to one of the following areas: human resources, finance, supply chain, research & development, customer development, marketing, and technology management.

The Unilever Future Leaders Programme is about making a big impact on the business. It is about growing iconic, market-leading brands from the first day and tapping into continuous business mentoring, excellent training, and hands-on responsibility. Graduates will have the chance to help Unilever build a better business and a better world, whilst finding their purpose to be their best self.

Graduates will have real responsibility from day one, an opportunity of becoming a manager after three years, and a great support network to see them develop and attain their future goals. Dependant on function, Unilever will support graduates in achieving Chartered status and qualifications.

With such a great ambition lie exciting challenges for the company and its brands, and a fantastic opportunity for graduates to have a great head start in their career, and to make a real difference to Unilever's business and the world!

GRADUATE VACANCIES IN 2020
ENGINEERING
FINANCE
HUMAN RESOURCES
LOGISTICS
MARKETING
RESEARCH & DEVELOPMENT
SALES
TECHNOLOGY

NUMBER OF VACANCIES
40-50 graduate jobs

LOCATIONS OF VACANCIES

STARTING SALARY FOR 2020
£32,000
Plus a £5,000 interest-free loan repayable over a three-year period, a £500 joining bonus for a Master's, and £2,000 for a PhD.

UNIVERSITY VISITS IN 2019-20
ASTON, BATH, BIRMINGHAM, BRISTOL, CAMBRIDGE, DURHAM, EXETER, IMPERIAL COLLEGE LONDON, KING'S COLLEGE LONDON, LANCASTER, LEEDS, LIVERPOOL, LOUGHBOROUGH, MANCHESTER, NEWCASTLE, NOTTINGHAM, OXFORD, SHEFFIELD, STRATHCLYDE, UNIVERSITY COLLEGE LONDON, WARWICK
Please check with your university careers service for full details of local events.

APPLICATION DEADLINE
10th November 2019

FURTHER INFORMATION
www.Top100GraduateEmployers.com
Register now for the latest news, campus events, work experience and graduate vacancies at Unilever.

CHANGE
LED BY YOU

A BETTER BUSINESS. A BETTER WORLD. A BETTER YOU.

JOIN NOW **UNILEVER.CO.UK/CAREERS/GRADUATES**

Unlocked

Unlocked Graduates is a two-year programme that is putting brilliant graduates at the heart of prison reform. Nearly half of all prisoners reoffend within a year of release, creating yet more victims and costing the UK more than £15bn. Unlocked's solution is a unique leadership programme.

The problems facing prisons are some of the most complex in society. Graduates on the Unlocked Leadership Programme need to be ambitious problem-solvers who are willing to hone their skills in leadership and communication on the frontline while also thinking about the big picture. Gathering intelligence and using their negotiation skills whether on the landing or in the Governor's office.

As well as the skills and experience gained from working, participants receive the support of a Mentoring Prison Officer; a competitive salary and development opportunities with partners such as Clifford Chance and the Ministry of Justice.

Unlocked is looking for graduates who can help shape the whole system for the better. That's why, as part of the programme, participants do a fully-funded, bespoke Master's degree. Combining academic study with real-world experience provides the tools to trial and assess solutions within their prisons. In the second year, participants have the opportunity to contribute to a policy paper and present the findings to the Ministry of Justice.

As a prison officer, no two days are the same. Helping some of the most vulnerable and challenging people in society means always being prepared for new situations, and being an advocate, negotiator, diplomat and leader.

Following the programme, Unlocked will continue to support participants – whether they stay in the prison system or leave it – to be part of a growing network of change-making alumni. Being a prison officer is about so much more than locking up – and with Unlocked Graduates, it can really open doors.

GRADUATE VACANCIES IN 2020
PRISON OFFICER

NUMBER OF VACANCIES
130 graduate jobs

LOCATIONS OF VACANCIES

STARTING SALARY FOR 2020
£22,000-£30,000
Dependent on location.

UNIVERSITY VISITS IN 2019-20
ASTON, BATH, BIRMINGHAM, BRISTOL, BRUNEL, CAMBRIDGE, CARDIFF, DURHAM, EDINBURGH, ESSEX, EXETER, KING'S COLLEGE LONDON, KENT, LANCASTER, LEEDS, LEICESTER, LIVERPOOL, LONDON SCHOOL OF ECONOMICS, LOUGHBOROUGH, MANCHESTER, NEWCASTLE, NOTTINGHAM, OXFORD, QUEEN MARY LONDON, READING, ROYAL HOLLOWAY, SCHOOL OF AFRICAN STUDIES, SHEFFIELD, SOUTHAMPTON, SURREY, SUSSEX, UEA, UNIVERSITY COLLEGE LONDON, WARWICK, YORK
Please check with your university careers service for full details of local events.

MINIMUM ENTRY REQUIREMENTS
2.1 Degree

APPLICATION DEADLINE
September-December 2019
Early application advised.

FURTHER INFORMATION
www.Top100GraduateEmployers.com
Register now for the latest news, campus events, work experience and graduate vacancies at Unlocked.

KARAN, 2019 COHORT
HM PRISON SERVICE
HC 275
THE BEST PART OF MY JOB?
HELPING PRISONERS ESCAPE.
unlockedgrads.org.uk

Virgin Media is part of Liberty Global plc, the world's largest international TV and broadband company. Connecting over 22 million customers through operations in 10 countries across Europe subscribing to more than 46 million TV, broadband internet and telephony services.

Across the UK and Ireland, Virgin Media offer four multi award-winning services: broadband, TV, mobile and home phone. Connecting millions of homes and businesses. Building tomorrow's communities. Creating jobs and transforming lives. Boosting the infrastructure and economy across the UK and Ireland.

Virgin Media are in the process of growing all parts of the business to connect more customers to the things and to the people they care about.

This unified global programme, across the Liberty Global and Virgin Media footprint, is designed to give graduates and placement students the knowledge, skills, experience and exposure needed to not only progress and develop a rewarding career but empower people to feel valued, limitless and inspired to help build connections that really matter.

Whether a candidate sees the future in technology & innovation, finance, or another of the amazing schemes, Virgin Media believes that anything is possible and encourages its graduates to lead with purpose, embodying the company values, seizing opportunities and gaining invaluable experience.

Graduates are important in supporting Virgin Media's future workforce capability needs, representing the diversity of customers and communities. Through this nurturing and engaging environment, most importantly Virgin Media is committed to helping future talent move around the organisation.

Why not join Virgin Media – unlock-ing a future career at one of the world's most exciting companies!

GRADUATE VACANCIES IN 2020
ENGINEERING
FINANCE
GENERAL MANAGEMENT
HUMAN RESOURCES
MARKETING
SALES
TECHNOLOGY

NUMBER OF VACANCIES
60+ graduate jobs

LOCATIONS OF VACANCIES

Vacancies also available in Europe.

STARTING SALARY FOR 2020
£30,000
Varies by function.
Plus a £2,000 welcome bonus.

UNIVERSITY VISITS IN 2019-20
ASTON, BATH, BIRMINGHAM, DURHAM, EXETER, IMPERIAL COLLEGE LONDON, LEEDS, LOUGHBOROUGH, MANCHESTER, READING, SHEFFIELD, SOUTHAMPTON, WARWICK
Please check with your university careers service for full details of local events.

MINIMUM ENTRY REQUIREMENTS
2.1 Degree

APPLICATION DEADLINE
Varies by function

FURTHER INFORMATION
www.Top100GraduateEmployers.com
Register now for the latest news, campus events, work experience and graduate vacancies at Virgin Media.

unlimiting

unlock-ing
your future career

We're spirited, brave and progressive,
standing out in a world of same-same.

Join us at
virg.in/futurecareers

facebook.com/VodafoneUKLife **f**   graduate.recruitment@vodafone.com ✉

linkedin.com/company/vodafone **in**   twitter.com/VodafoneUKLife 🐦

instagram.com/VodafoneUKLife 📷   youtube.com/VodafoneUKLife ▶

GRADUATE VACANCIES IN 2020

FINANCE
HUMAN RESOURCES
TECHNOLOGY

NUMBER OF VACANCIES
149 graduate jobs

LOCATIONS OF VACANCIES

STARTING SALARY FOR 2020
£33,000
For Technology roles.

£30,000
For non-Technology roles.

UNIVERSITY VISITS IN 2019-20
BATH, BIRMINGHAM, BRISTOL, CAMBRIDGE,
CARDIFF, DURHAM, EDINBURGH, EXETER,
GLASGOW, IMPERIAL COLLEGE LONDON,
KING'S COLLEGE LONDON, LANCASTER,
LEEDS, LONDON SCHOOL OF ECONOMICS,
LOUGHBOROUGH, MANCHESTER,
NOTTINGHAM, OXFORD, QUEEN MARY
LONDON, READING, ROYAL HOLLOWAY,
SHEFFIELD, SOUTHAMPTON, ST ANDREWS,
SURREY, UNIVERSITY COLLEGE LONDON,
WARWICK, YORK
*Please check with your university careers
service for full details of local events.*

MINIMUM ENTRY REQUIREMENTS
2.2 Degree

APPLICATION DEADLINE
31st December 2019

FURTHER INFORMATION
www.Top100GraduateEmployers.com
*Register now for the latest news, campus
events, work experience and graduate
vacancies at Vodafone.*

As a global tech leader, Vodafone transforms businesses and millions of lives around the world every day. From providing superfast network speed to smartphones to drones that deliver phone signal, they're behind some of the world's greatest tech achievements. There's never been a more exciting time to join.

The company pride themselves on developing early careers. Its Discover Graduate Scheme allows graduates to gain hands-on experience and skills from exceptional people at a company that's beating other game changers in the industry. Its two-year programme covers specialisms such as Digital, Tech, Finance and HR, with business exposure in specialist and generalist areas for a breadth of exposure. If a graduate has a particular area of interest, there's full support to develop and progress in that direction.

Vodafone also offers a scope and scale that few can rival, operating in 26 countries and in partnership with networks in over 55 more. It's a chance to be part of a global community of graduates that are revolutionising communications through technology and innovation. Because of the nature of their business, constant evolution underpins everything Vodafone does, making for a fast-paced, dynamic and vibrant place to work. Its stunning variety of projects includes giving children in refugee camps access to instant classroom technology and utilising the internet of things to modernise farming techniques.

Vodafone relies on a huge mix of people and skills to achieve its ambitious goals. They're looking for graduates who are creative, analytical and adaptable by nature. People who are excited by the possibilities of technology and the positive impact it can have across the globe. Joining its scheme means being part of a truly diverse and inclusive group of like-minded people who want to change the world. The Future is Exciting. Ready?

Emergency phone signal delivered by drone. You in?

And that's just one of our revolutionary projects defining the future of tech and communications.

But we need exceptional graduates to make them happen. Join us, get hands-on experience across a huge range of specialities and be part of something extraordinary.

Discover our graduate opportunities –
careers.vodafone.com

The future is exciting.
Ready?

wellcome

Wellcome is an independent global charitable foundation that exists to improve health for everyone by helping great ideas to thrive. It supports researchers, takes on big health challenges, campaigns for better science, and helps everyone get involved with science and health research.

Wellcome supports transformative work, such as co-funding the development of a new Ebola vaccine, leading policy and campaign activity to promote change in mitochondrial donation, and launching Wellcome Collection – a museum and library exploring medicine, life and art. Wellcome is best known for funding scientific and medical research, but more broadly it works at the intersection of health and society, and so is looking for graduates from all backgrounds.

For recent graduates, Wellcome offers two-year development programmes. Their general programme gives experience of four different jobs for six months each. These could involve working with research centres in Africa and Asia, writing parliamentary briefings, or finding new ways to engage the public. Wellcome also offers career-specific programmes in areas such as investments for those ready to specialise. Whichever programme graduates choose, they'll be valued team members, with support from mentors, line managers and peers. They'll also benefit from training, real responsibilities, and the knowledge that they're contributing to improving the health of humanity.

The programmes encourage graduates to work outside of their comfort zone, to expand their career potential. At the end of the programmes many graduates go on to more senior roles at Wellcome, while others move to other charities, further study, cultural venues or even setting up their own businesses. Whatever graduates choose, Wellcome values ongoing relationships with its alumni so they can continue to make a difference in global health.

GRADUATE VACANCIES IN 2020

GENERAL MANAGEMENT
HUMAN RESOURCES
INVESTMENT BANKING
LAW
MEDIA
RESEARCH & DEVELOPMENT
TECHNOLOGY

NUMBER OF VACANCIES
12 graduate jobs

LOCATIONS OF VACANCIES

STARTING SALARY FOR 2020
£26,000

UNIVERSITY VISITS IN 2019-20
BATH, BIRMINGHAM, BRISTOL, CAMBRIDGE, EXETER, IMPERIAL COLLEGE LONDON, KING'S COLLEGE LONDON, KENT, LEEDS, LEICESTER, LONDON SCHOOL OF ECONOMICS, NOTTINGHAM, QUEEN MARY LONDON, ROYAL HOLLOWAY, SHEFFIELD, UEA, UNIVERSITY COLLEGE LONDON
Please check with your university careers service for full details of local events.

MINIMUM ENTRY REQUIREMENTS
2.2 Degree

FURTHER INFORMATION
www.Top100GraduateEmployers.com
*Register now for the latest news, campus events, work experience and graduate vacancies at **Wellcome**.*

"In an organisation as diverse as Wellcome, it could be the most varied two years of your whole career"

Isobel, joined Wellcome in 2018

White & Case is a global law firm with nearly 2,000 lawyers worldwide. They've built an enviable network of 44 offices in 30 countries. That investment is the foundation for their client work in 180 countries today. Many White & Case clients are multinational organisations with complex needs that require the involvement of multiple offices.

White & Case trainees will work on fast-paced, cutting-edge, cross-border projects from the outset of their career. In London, the key areas of work include: bank finance (including regulatory compliance); financial restructuring and insolvency; capital markets (high yield and securitisation); dispute resolution (including antitrust, commercial litigation, intellectual property, international arbitration, trade, white collar and construction and engineering); energy, infrastructure, project and asset finance (EIPAF); corporate (including M&A, private equity, employment, compensation and benefits, investment funds, real estate and tax).

White & Case is looking to recruit ambitious trainees who have a desire to gain hands-on practical experience from day one and a willingness to take charge of their own career. They value globally-minded citizens of the world who are eager to work across borders and cultures, and who are intrigued by solving problems within multiple legal systems.

The training contract consists of four six-month seats, one of which is guaranteed to be spent in one of their overseas offices, including Abu Dhabi, Beijing, Brussels, Dubai, Frankfurt, Geneva, Hong Kong, Johannesburg, Moscow, New York, Paris, Prague, Singapore, Stockholm, Tokyo. The remaining three seats can be spent in any one of the firm's practice groups in London. Receiving a high level of partner and senior associate contact from day one, trainees can be confident that they will receive high-quality, stimulating and rewarding work.

GRADUATE VACANCIES IN 2020
LAW

NUMBER OF VACANCIES
50 graduate jobs
For training contracts starting in 2022.

LOCATIONS OF VACANCIES

STARTING SALARY FOR 2020
£48,000

UNIVERSITY VISITS IN 2019-20
BIRMINGHAM, BRISTOL, CAMBRIDGE, DURHAM, EDINBURGH, EXETER, KING'S COLLEGE LONDON, LANCASTER, LEEDS, LEICESTER, LONDON SCHOOL OF ECONOMICS, MANCHESTER, NEWCASTLE, NOTTINGHAM, OXFORD, QUEEN MARY LONDON, SCHOOL OF AFRICAN STUDIES, SOUTHAMPTON, ST ANDREWS, UNIVERSITY COLLEGE LONDON, WARWICK, YORK
Please check with your university careers service for full details of local events.

MINIMUM ENTRY REQUIREMENTS
2.1 Degree

APPLICATION DEADLINE
Please see website for full details.

FURTHER INFORMATION
www.Top100GraduateEmployers.com
Register now for the latest news, campus events, work experience and graduate vacancies at White & Case.